Mindfulness JOURNAL FOR

Teen girls

a guide To becoMing a calMer, happier Version of yourself Through Mindfulness Journaling and daily PracTice.

Teen Thrive

medical disclaimer

This book does not contain medical information [medical information referring to mental and physical health throughout his disclaimer] or health advice. The health information contained in this book is provided for general information and educational purposes only and is not intended as and shall not be understood or construed as professional medical advice, diagnosis, or treatment or substitute for professional medical advice, diagnosis, or treatment. Before taking any action based upon such information, we expressly recommend that you seek advice from medical professionals.

Your use of the book, including the implementation of any suggestions or recommendations laid out in the book, does not create a doctor-patient relationship. Your use of the book is solely at your own risk. You expressly agree not to rely upon any information contained in the book as a substitute for professional medical advice, diagnosis, or treatment.

Under no circumstances shall Teen Thrive be held liable or responsible for any errors or omissions in the book or for any damage you may suffer with respect to any actions taken or not taken based on any or all of the contents of the book and/ or as a result of failing to seek competent advice from medical professionals.

A LITTLE ABOUT ME

NAME :

ADDRESS :

PHONE :

INSTAGRAM :

FACEBOOK :

EMAIL :

Table of contents

i. So, how do I use this journal?
v   When to seek additional support

PART 1: MINDFULNESS 101   1-54

CHAPTER 1
WHAT IS MINDFULNESS?   1

CHAPTER 2
CREATING MY MINDFULNESS PRACTICE   5

CHAPTER 3
BEING PRESENT TODAY   14

CHAPTER 4
LEARNING TO BE HONEST WITH MYSELF   28

CHAPTER 5
GRATITUDE & MINDFULNESS   39

EVEN MORE MINDFULNESS EXERCISES   42-54

PART 2: DAILY MINDFULNESS JOURNAL PAGES   55-115

Works cited   116

A brief message from teen thrive   118

HOW DO I USE THIS JOURNAL?

Step One

LEARN MORE ABOUT MINDFULNESS BEFORE YOU START JOURNALING.

This book is not just a journal, it is a guide that will help you understand more about mindfulness and help you build a daily mindfulness routine [or practice] that will really make a difference in your life.

Step two

START BUILDING YOUR MINDFULNESS PRACTICE

After you've learned more about what mindfulness is, use this guide to carve out the type of mindfulness practice you'd like to do on a daily basis. We've given you loads of tips and tools for how to do this.

Step three

CREATE A MINDFULNESS CORNER IN YOUR ROOM.

If you want your mindfulness practice to make a difference in how you see yourself and the world around you, you must be in a calm, warm, and safe space. For instance, you could make sure your favorite slippers are close by, play some calming music, and post some positive sayings on your wall.

step four

DECIDE WHEN YOU WANT TO DO YOUR MINDFULNESS ROUTINE AND STICK TO IT.

It's really important to put aside a specific time and place for you to complete your mindfulness routine [for best results, it should be daily]. If you don't do this, you'll likely forget.

step five

TAKE A FEW DEEP BREATHS

Before you start each new mindfulness exercise, take a few deep breaths and close your eyes. This will 'ground' you in the present and take your mind off the worries, fears, responsibilities, and to-do lists constantly swirling around in your head.

step six
REFLECT ON YOUR DAY

Reflect on the day that either just passed or that is about to happen. Review your thoughts, feelings, doubts, fears, and joys. Allow yourself to be honest, and don't place 'labels' on your thoughts and feelings.

step seven
FREELY EXPRESS YOURSELF & BE KIND

Don't be afraid to express yourself with honesty and openness. Remember: you've created this routine, and you've made your space comfortable and safe. Be kind to yourself as you learn more about yourself. And don't be too hard on yourself if you miss one day. Just start again tomorrow.

step eight
LOOK BACK AT PREVIOUS ENTRIES

Remember to read your past journal entries. You'll either see some serious growth and change and be encouraged, or you'll be reminded that you've still got some lessons to learn [Don't we all!].

WHEN MINDFULNESS ISN'T ENOUGH

HOW DO I KNOW WHEN I NEED TO GET SOME EXTRA HELP?

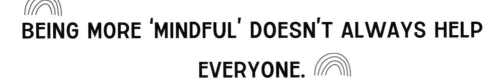

BEING MORE 'MINDFUL' DOESN'T ALWAYS HELP EVERYONE.

You might find that after three months of being super consistent with your mindfulness practice, you are still highly stressed, worried, anxious, and uncomfortable in your own skin. And that is a sure sign that you should reach out to friends, family, and even professional therapists to help you process your emotions and get to the root of the issue.

Here are some steps that you can take:

1. TALK TO A TRUSTED ADULT IN YOUR LIFE [A FAMILY FRIEND, PARENT, TEACHER, SCHOOL COUNSELOR, SPORTS COACH, ETC.]
2. SEE IF THERE ARE ANY LICENSED THERAPISTS IN YOUR AREA THAT SPECIALIZE IN WORKING WITH TEENS.
3. CONTINUE WITH THE MINDFULNESS PRACTICE THAT YOU'VE ALREADY ESTABLISHED, EVEN IF YOU DON'T THINK IT'S HELPING.

PART 1

Mindfulness 101

CHAPTER 1

~~~~~~~~~~

SO, WHAT IS MINDFULNESS?

~~~~~~~~~~

BEING MORE MINDFUL HELPS YOU TO FOCUS ON WHAT YOU'RE EXPERIENCING RIGHT NOW WITHOUT JUDGMENT OR DISTRACTION.

And it really helps your mind, body, and soul slow down.

Your life is likely super fast-paced. You're probably juggling school work, maybe a part-time job, finding time to spend with your friends, and planning ahead for your future. Oh, and plus, managing your home life. That's a lot! And it's only going to get busier as you transition into adulthood and are out on your own.

That's why it's so important to develop these mindfulness strategies now. Your daily mindfulness routine can be the time that you set aside for taking care of your mental health and 'centering yourself' on peaceful and carefree thoughts. We all need that!

What does being 'fully present' mean?

It means stopping your thoughts and emotions dead in their tracks and just 'being.' In those moments, you notice what you are sensing [seeing, hearing, touching, smelling, tasting], and you recognize the beauty that is all around you.

Don't think you're very 'mindful' right now? That's ok. Just like everything in life, you can learn.

HERE'S HOW:

Start developing your mindfulness skills by completing the mindfulness activities in this book, like the technology detox, guided meditations, the nature walk, writing a letter to yourself, and more.

All of these activities teach you how to train your mind, body, and soul to put away distractions and focus on the small things in life that can bring you peace and joy.

HERE ARE A FEW KEY ASPECTS OF MINDFULNESS:

NO LABELING

Teach yourself how to reflect on your thoughts, emotions, and experiences without calling them good or bad. There is a time and place for that, but not while you are trying to calm your mind, body and soul. Simply recognize what you are thinking, feeling and experiencing, and accept it for what it is.

BEING CENTERED IN THE PRESENT

Pay close attention to what you are doing, saying, thinking, feeling, and sensing right now; not on what happened in the past or what is going to happen in the future.

ACCEPTANCE AND SELF-COMPASSION:

Accept yourself for who you are and have some compassion for yourself when you have an 'off' day or when your weaknesses are obvious. We all have weaknesses and strengths. Allow yourself the time you need to work through things.

THE BENEFITS

YOU'LL BE ABLE TO FOCUS MORE

The more you practice your mindfulness routine, the more you are focusing on the present.
And soon, you'll see that focusing on other things ,like school work, is pretty simple.

YOU'LL BE MORE AWARE OF WHO YOU ARE AND WHAT YOU'RE FEELING,

After starting your mindfulness practice, you'll learn a ton of stuff about how you process what others say to you. You'll know what makes you 'tick' and what 'triggers' you. And after keeping a record of these thoughts, and feelings, you'll know how to help yourself in those moments.

YOU'RE LIKELY TO HAVE LESS STRESS

There have been tons of studies by psychologists and psychiatrists that show that having a long-term mindfulness practice in place can help reduce stress and make a person more relaxed. Sounds great, right?

CHAPTER 2

〰〰〰〰〰〰〰〰〰

CREATING MY MINDFULNESS PRACTICE

〰〰〰〰〰〰〰〰〰

Ok, so now you have a bit of an idea of what we mean by mindfulness. But what's a mindfulness practice?

A MINDFULNESS PRACTICE IS SOMETHING YOU DO EVERY SINGLE DAY TO ENCOURAGE YOUR MIND, BODY, AND SOUL TO BE PRESENT, AND TO FOCUS ON THE SMALL JOYS IN LIFE.

A mindfulness practice is a plan you make with yourself and will depend on how much time you want to devote to it per day and what types of activities you are comfortable doing. This means that you can devote as much or as little time to your practice as you'd like and incorporate as many 'activities' as you'd like. It's completely up to you. But here are some rules that you should follow when creating your plan:

BE CONSISTENT: SET UP YOUR MINDFULNESS PRACTICE SO THAT YOU ARE ABLE TO DO IT AT THE SAME TIME EVERY DAY AND FOR THE SAME AMOUNT OF TIME. BY DOING THIS, YOU'RE TRAINING YOUR BODY AND MIND TO BE 'IN THE ZONE' AT THE RIGHT TIME.

CHOOSE A QUIET SPACE TO DO YOUR MINDFULNESS PRACTICE WHERE YOU WON'T BE BOTHERED OR DISTRACTED.

STAY WITHIN YOUR COMFORT ZONE: CHOOSE ACTIVITIES THAT YOU KNOW YOU ARE COMFORTABLE WITH.

HAVE A WAY OF TRACKING YOUR PROGRESS: RECORD AUDIO REFLECTIONS, WRITE IN YOUR JOURNAL, DRAW, OR FIND ANOTHER WAY TO TRACK YOUR PROGRESS.

MINDFULNESS STRATEGIES
FOR STRESSFUL SITUATIONS

HAVE YOU EVER BEEN CAUGHT OFF GUARD BY A SUPER STRESSFUL SITUATION IN THE MIDDLE OF YOUR DAY? MAYBE YOU HAD A PRESENTATION IN A CLASS THAT YOU COMPLETELY FORGOT ABOUT AND WEREN'T PREPARED FOR. OR MAYBE YOU HAD BEEN AVOIDING A CLASSMATE FOR A WHILE, AND SUDDENLY, YOU'RE ASSIGNED AS THEIR LAB PARTNER.

HERE ARE SOME SIMPLE MINDFULNESS STRATEGIES THAT CAN HELP YOU DEAL WITH STRESS:

DEEP BREATHING:

Take a few moments to focus on your breathing. Close your eyes [if you feel comfortable with that] and take slow, deep breaths. How does it feel when your breath leaves and enters your body? Allow this experience to calm your body.

BODY SCAN

Stay in that moment of relaxation, but now think about any areas of your body that feel tense or painful [often we feel stress in our shoulders, lower back, lower legs, etc.]. Then move on to the rest of your body and let go of the muscle tightness that you might be feeling. Stretch those areas out.

GROUNDING TECHNIQUES

Notice five things you can see, four things you can touch, three things you can hear, two things you can smell, and one thing you can taste. When you do this, you are no longer focusing your attention on stressful things, but on simple sensory experiences.

NON-JUDGMENTAL AWARENESS

Instead of getting caught up in the stress or trying to push it away, practice accepting and observing your thoughts, emotions, fears, doubts, and outward experiences.

SELF-COMPASSION

Remember to be kind to yourself while you are experiencing these stressors. Don't have too many expectations. Just allow yourself to work through it.

REFRAME PERSPECTIVE

Take a moment and think about this situation from an outsider's perspective. Is there anything about the situation that you might have misinterpreted? Are there any biases you bring? Do you have any control or influence over the situation? If not, focus on what you can do to take care of yourself and make the situation better.

ENGAGE IN MINDFUL ACTIVITIES

If these bite-sized strategies don't help much, you'll want to make time later for a lengthier mindfulness activity. This could include coloring, journaling, listening to calming music, practicing yoga or stretching, or going for a walk. The goal is to give yourself a sense of calm and release from the stressor.

HERE'S A SAMPLE OF WHAT YOUR MINDFULNESS PRACTICE COULD LOOK LIKE:

my daily
MINDFULNESS PRACTICE

MY MINDFULNESS PRACTICE WILL START ON *Saturday July 1*

(AM)/PM   (AM)/PM

MY PRACTICE WILL START EVERYDAY AT: `8:00`   AND END AT   `8:30`

AND DURING MY PRACTICE WILL BE:

[ ] DRAWING

Silencing my thoughts for 5 minutes straight

[✓] **REFLECTING IN MY JOURNAL**

[ ] **GETTING OUTSIDE INTO NATURE**

[✓] **FOCUSING ON MY BREATHING**

MY MINDFULNESS SPACE

I'VE ALREADY SET UP MY MINDFULNESS SPACE AND THIS IS WHAT IS LOOKS LIKE ⟶

[✓] I STILL NEED TO THINK ABOUT WHAT I WANT MY MINDFULNESS SPACE TO LOOK LIKE, BUT HERE ARE MY IDEAS ⟶

my mindfulness space will be in my bedroom

I'm going to set up some pillows in my window seat.

and ask my mom to buy me some essential oils and a diffuser.

EXERCISE # 1 : MY DAILY MINDFULNESS PRACTICE

my daily
MINDFULNESS PRACTICE

NOW IT'S YOUR TURN TO FILL IT IN:

MY MINDFULNESS PRACTICE WILL START ON

AM/ PM   AM/ PM

MY PRACTICE WILL START EVERYDAY AT: AND END AT

AND DURING MY PRACTICE WILL BE:

_____   ☐ DRAWING

_____   ☐ REFLECTING IN MY JOURNAL

_____   ☐ GETTING OUTSIDE INTO NATURE

_____   ☐ FOCUSING ON MY BREATHING

MY MINDFULNESS SPACE

I'VE ALREADY SET UP MY
MINDFULNESS SPACE AND
THIS IS WHAT IS LOOKS
LIKE ⟶

☐ I STILL NEED TO THINK
ABOUT WHAT I WANT MY
MINDFULNESS SPACE TO
LOOK LIKE, BUT HERE ARE
MY IDEAS ⟶

_____

_____

_____

_____

FINDING PEACE WHERE I AM
guided meditation

Let's try out a simple mindfulness activity before we dive deeper. If this is your first mindfulness activity, don't forget to journal about your thoughts and feelings during and after this activity.

prepare yourself

Welcome to this guided meditation, which is designed to help you find peace, relaxation, and self-empowerment.

Find a comfortable position, either sitting or lying down, and gently close your eyes. Take a deep breath in, and slowly exhale, letting go of any tension or stress you may be holding onto. Allow your body to relax completely.

here we go.....

Bring your attention to your breathing. Think about the natural rhythm of your breath as you inhale and exhale.

As you continue to breathe, close your eyes. Imagine a warm, golden light all around you. This light is your inner strength. As you breathe in and out, the light becomes warmer and brighter until you are wrapped in it like a cozy blanket.

You are strong, and you can get through anything. There are so many things to love about yourself. Think about something that you appreciate about yourself. It could be a physical attribute, a talent, or a positive personality trait. Think about all the good things about yourself and how they have helped those around you.

Your light is bright, and it stretches out. Imagine your light is extending to other teen girls in your life. Visualize this: a sea of teen girls, all glowing with bright lights. These lights represent love, beauty, and self-acceptance. You are not alone in your journey.

Take a moment to reflect on the challenges and pressures you are facing. Recognize that these challenges are opportunities for growth and learning. You have the strength to overcome any obstacles that come your way. Trust in your abilities and believe in yourself.

Now, envision yourself as a confident and successful young woman. See yourself achieving your goals, pursuing your passions, and positively impacting the world. Hold onto this vision and let it inspire and motivate you.

As we near the end of this meditation, remember this: you deserve to be loved. And you deserve to experience joy in your life.

Gently think about your breath, feeling the rise and fall of your chest. Wiggle your fingers and toes, slowly awakening your body. When you're ready, open your eyes, feeling refreshed and empowered.

WHAT WERE YOU THINKING AND FEELING DURING THIS MEDITATION? AND AFTERWARDS?

_____

_____

_____

_____

_____

_____

WANT TO CREATE YOUR OWN GUIDED MEDITATION? WRITE YOUR OWN HERE....

_____

_____

_____

_____

_____

_____

CHAPTER 3

BEING PRESENT TODAY

Okay, so in the first chapter, we very briefly mentioned that one of the most important parts of your mindfulness practice is the idea of 'being present.' We are going to talk more about that now. So what does it mean to 'be present'?

TO BE PRESENT MEANS TO CENTER YOUR MIND, BODY, AND SOUL ON WHAT YOU ARE SEEING, TOUCHING, SMELLING, HEARING, AND OTHERWISE SENSING AROUND YOU AT THE PRESENT TIME.

This concept is the opposite of filling your mind with things that stress you out, especially things that aren't within your control right now. When you are 'present,' you are emptying your mind of thoughts about the future and thinking only about what you are experiencing right now.

I'm sure you can imagine how this can make you feel calmer and help you to appreciate the beautiful things around you, the loving and supportive people in your life, and the 'little' joys in life [like when your mom makes you French toast for breakfast even on a school day.]

COLOR ME!

WORRY LESS
APPRECIATE MORE
BE PRESENT

HERE ARE SOME WAYS THAT YOU CAN BE PRESENT TODAY:

put away the things that distract you

WHEN SPENDING TIME WITH OTHERS, PUT AWAY THE THINGS THAT OFTEN DISTRACT YOU, WHETHER THEY ARE ELECTRONIC DEVICES OR NOT. INSTEAD, GIVE ALL OF YOUR ATTENTION TO THE PEOPLE YOU ARE WITH.

focus on what people are saying

WHEN HAVING CONVERSATIONS WITH FRIENDS, FAMILY, OR CLASSMATES, LISTEN TO WHAT THEY ARE SAYING. AVOID INTERRUPTING THEM OR THINKING ABOUT YOUR RESPONSE WHILE THEY ARE SPEAKING.

notice and appreciate the small things in life

TAKE A MOMENT TO NOTICE AND APPRECIATE THE SMALL DETAILS IN YOUR SURROUNDINGS. WHETHER IT'S THE BEAUTY OF NATURE, THE TASTE OF YOUR FOOD, OR THE SOUND OF MUSIC, FOCUS ON THE PRESENT EXPERIENCE.

slow down and take a deep breath

TAKE SLOW, DEEP BREATHS TO ANCHOR YOURSELF IN THE PRESENT MOMENT. THIS CAN HELP CALM YOUR MIND, REDUCE STRESS, AND INCREASE YOUR AWARENESS OF WHAT IS HAPPENING AROUND YOU.

take a break from technology

TO MAKE THIS EASIER ON YOU, WE'VE INCLUDED A GUIDE TO A TECHNOLOGY DETOX AND A PLACE WHERE YOU CAN PLAN OUT YOUR FUTURE TECHNOLOGY DETOXES.

be grateful

THINK ABOUT THE THINGS YOU ARE GRATEFUL FOR IN YOUR LIFE. FOCUS ON THE POSITIVE ASPECTS OF YOUR PRESENT CIRCUMSTANCES.

be mindful no matter what you're doing

TRY TO DO IT WITH FULL AWARENESS, WHETHER YOU'RE STUDYING, EXERCISING, OR ENGAGING IN A HOBBY. PAY ATTENTION TO THE TASK AT HAND RATHER THAN LETTING YOUR MIND WANDER TO THE PAST OR FUTURE.

take care of yourself

TAKING CARE OF YOUR PHYSICAL, EMOTIONAL, AND MENTAL WELL-BEING IS ESSENTIAL FOR BEING PRESENT. MAKE TIME FOR ACTIVITIES THAT NOURISH YOU, SUCH AS GETTING ENOUGH SLEEP, EATING NUTRITIOUS MEALS, AND DOING THINGS THAT MAKE YOU HAPPY.

3-DAY TECHNOLOGY DETOX EXERCISE

DAY ONE

Prepare Yourself:

UNDERSTAND WHY YOU ARE DOING IT, WHETHER IT'S TO REDUCE SCREEN TIME, IMPROVE FOCUS, OR RECONNECT WITH YOURSELF. WRITE DOWN YOUR GOALS AND KEEP THEM IN MIND THROUGHOUT THE DETOX.

Start your Device Detox:

START BY PUTTING YOUR DEVICES IN A DESIGNATED SPOT OR A DRAWER WHERE YOU WON'T SEE THEM MUCH. YOU DON'T WANT TO TEMPT YOURSELF. THESE ARE THE DEVICES THAT YOU SHOULD BE PUTTING AWAY: SMARTPHONE, TABLET, COMPUTER, AND ANY OTHER ELECTRONIC DEVICES YOU TYPICALLY USE. AVOID USING THEM FOR THE DURATION OF THE DETOX.

Establish Offline Activities:

PLAN ACTIVITIES THAT DON'T INVOLVE YOUR DEVICES. THIS COULD INCLUDE READING BOOKS, DRAWING, JOURNALING, ENGAGING IN HOBBIES, SPENDING TIME OUTDOORS, OR CONNECTING WITH FRIENDS AND FAMILY FACE-TO-FACE.

TECHNOLOGY
DETOX EXERCISE

DAY TWO

Start Your Day With A mindfulness Activity

INSTEAD OF REACHING FOR YOUR PHONE, BEGIN WITH A FEW MINUTES OF MEDITATION, DEEP BREATHING EXERCISES, OR STRETCHING. FOCUS ON THE HERE AND NOW. BREATH DEEPLY. TOUCH. SMELL. TASTE. TAKE IN THE BEAUTY THAT IS AROUND YOU.

Be Creative

PAINT, WRITE, OR PLAY A MUSICAL INSTRUMENT. GET LOST IN THE FLOW OF YOUR CHOSEN CREATIVE OUTLET, ALLOWING YOUR MIND TO WANDER AND EXPLORE NEW IDEAS.

Spend Quality Time with Others

CONNECT WITH FRIENDS AND FAMILY IN PERSON. HAVE MEANINGFUL CONVERSATIONS, PLAY GAMES, OR GO DO SOMETHING SPECIAL TOGETHER. ENJOY THE COMPANY AND STRENGTHEN YOUR RELATIONSHIPS WITHOUT THE DISTRACTION OF TECHNOLOGY.

Connect with Nature

GO FOR A WALK, HIKE, OR BIKE RIDE. TAKE IN THE SIGHTS, SOUNDS, AND SMELLS OF THE NATURAL WORLD AROUND YOU. ALLOW YOURSELF TO APPRECIATE THE BEAUTY AND SERENITY OF YOUR SURROUNDINGS.

EXERCISE # 3 : THREE DAY TECHNOLOGY DETOX

TECHNOLOGY
DETOX EXERCISE

DAY THREE

Self-Reflect

WRITE A JOURNAL ABOUT YOUR EXPERIENCES DURING THE TECHNOLOGY DETOX. TAKE NOTE OF ANY OF YOUR INSIGHTS, EMOTIONS, OR REALIZATIONS. REFLECT ON THE IMPACT OF TECHNOLOGY IN YOUR LIFE AND HOW THESE LAST FEW DAYS HAVE CHANGED YOU.

Be Grateful

BEFORE CONCLUDING YOUR TECHNOLOGY DETOX, EXPRESS GRATITUDE FOR THE EXPERIENCE. REFLECT ON THE BENEFITS YOU'VE GAINED, THE MOMENTS OF JOY AND CONNECTION, AND THE GROWTH YOU'VE EXPERIENCED DURING THIS TIME. WRITE DOWN THREE THINGS YOU ARE GRATEFUL FOR AS A REMINDER OF THE POSITIVE IMPACT OF THE DETOX.

Get Active

ENGAGE IN PHYSICAL EXERCISE TO ENERGIZE YOUR BODY AND MIND. GO FOR A RUN, DO A WORKOUT ROUTINE, OR TRY A NEW SPORT. PHYSICAL ACTIVITY HELPS REDUCE STRESS, BOOSTS YOUR MOOD, AND IMPROVES OVERALL WELL-BEING.

Do Something Enjoyable

READ A CAPTIVATING BOOK, SOLVE PUZZLES, PLAY BOARD GAMES, OR ENGAGE IN DIY PROJECTS. DISCOVER NEW WAYS TO ENTERTAIN YOURSELF THAT STIMULATE YOUR MIND AND IMAGINATION.

Ok so I've completed the technology detox
NOW WHAT?

HERE ARE SOME THINGS YOU CAN TO MAKE SURE YOU GET THE MOST OUT OF YOUR EXPERIENCE.....

REFLECT ON THE EXPERIENCE:

Take some time to reflect on your experience during the technology detox. Consider how it felt to disconnect from technology, any challenges you faced, and any positive changes you noticed in yourself or your surroundings.

IDENTIFY BENEFITS AND LESSONS

Reflect on what you learned. Did you notice any changes in your focus, mood, or relationships? Did you discover new activities or interests? Write down the positive outcomes and insights you gained from your experience.

TECHNOLOGY MOVING FORWARD...

Based on your reflections and the benefits you experienced, set intentions for how you want to integrate technology into your life moving forward. Consider how you can create a healthier relationship with technology, balancing its benefits while also setting boundaries to prevent yourself from being glued to a screen. Write down your intentions in your journal as a reminder and guide.

CREATE A TECHNOLOGY USE PLAN:

Decide how and when you will use technology in a mindful and intentional way. Establish guidelines and boundaries for yourself, such as setting specific times for device usage, designating tech-free zones, or implementing regular digital detox periods. Write down your plan in your journal as a reference. Check out page 31

PRACTICE MINDFUL TECHNOLOGY USE:

As you start using technology again, set boundaries, such as turning off notifications or practicing mindful breaks during extended screen time. Use your journal to reflect on your experiences and make adjustments as needed.

MY TECHNOLOGY usage plan

Lately I've been having too much screen time. Here's what I'm going to do about it

➡️ _____

_____

_____

_____

STARTING _____ (DATE)   I'm going to turn off my devices

FROM _____ : ____ AM/ PM

TO _____ : ____ AM/ PM

and instead I'm going to:

_____

_____

_____

_____

MY
TECHNOLOGY usage plan

And when I am
using technology
I'm going to
work on:

EXAMPLE: LOWERING HOW OFTEN I CHECK
MY FACEBOOK FEED

_____

_____

_____

I know _____ is not a great
place to hang out
online.

[specific site, social media platform, video game]

because right after I visit the site, play the game or look at
my feed I feel:

so now my
plan is to

- [ ] TELL MY FRIENDS I'M NOT INTO IT ANYMORE
- [ ] DELETE MY ACCOUNT
- [ ] LIMIT MY USE OF THE SITE, VIDEO CAME OR SOCIAL MEDIA
- [ ] I'M NOT SURE WHAT MY PLAN IS GOING TO BE
- [ ] PROBABLY JUST DO IT ANYWAY

CENTER YOUR BODY IN THE PRESENT

RELAX

a guided meditation

WELCOME TO THIS GUIDED MEDITATION, DESIGNED TO HELP YOU FOCUS ON THE HERE AND NOW. LET YOUR BODY RELAX WITH THESE GUIDED BREATHING EXERCISES AND EXPERIENCE INNER RENEWAL.

prepare yourself

Begin by finding a quiet and comfortable space where you can relax and unwind. Sit or lie down in a position that feels comfortable to you, allowing your body to settle into a relaxed posture. Take a moment to adjust your position and let go of any tension in your body.

here we go....

EXERCISE # 5 : CENTER YOUR BODY GUIDED MEDITATION

just relax

Now, gently close your eyes and take a deep breath through your nose, allowing your belly to expand. As you exhale through your mouth, release any stress or worries you may carry with you. Take a few more deep breaths like this, breathing in relaxation and breathing out any tension or negative energy.

Bring your attention to the present moment, to this space and time just for yourself. Notice the sensations in your body—the weight of your body on the surface beneath you, the feeling of the air against your skin. Allow yourself to fully arrive in this present moment, letting go of the past and the future.

Now, shift your attention to your breath. Notice the natural flow of your breath, the gentle rise and fall of your chest, or the sensation of the breath entering and leaving your nostrils. Take a moment to fully connect with your breath, allowing it to anchor you to the present moment.

As you continue to breathe, I want you to imagine a beautiful garden. This garden is a sanctuary for you, a place of peace, tranquility, and natural beauty. Visualize this garden in your mind's eye. Observe the vibrant colors of the flowers, the lush greenery, and the clear blue sky above.

Take a moment to explore this garden with your imagination. As you walk through the garden, notice the different flowers and plants that catch your eye. Take in the scents of the flowers, the gentle rustling of leaves in the breeze, and the warmth of the sun on your skin.

In this garden, you feel completely safe, at peace, and surrounded by beauty. Take a few moments to simply be present in this space, soaking in the serenity and tranquility of the garden. Allow yourself to relax and let go of any worries or stresses.

RELAX

EXERCISE # 5 : CENTER YOUR BODY GUIDED MEDITATION

just relax

Now, I invite you to find a comfortable spot in this garden—a place where you can sit or lie down. As you settle into this spot, feel a sense of complete relaxation washing over you. Surrender to the peaceful energy of the garden and let go of any tension or discomfort in your body.

In this state of deep relaxation, take a moment to set an intention for yourself. What would you like to cultivate in your life? It could be self-compassion, confidence, peace, or anything else that resonates with you. Take a moment to silently repeat this intention to yourself, feeling it deeply in your heart.

Now, take a few more deep breaths, breathing in this intention and allowing it to infuse every cell of your being. And as you exhale, release any doubts or obstacles that may be standing in the way of manifesting this intention.

Take a moment to appreciate yourself for dedicating this time to self-care and inner exploration. You are deserving of this peace and tranquility. As we come to the end of this meditation, take a moment to express gratitude for this moment, for the garden within your mind, and for yourself.

When you are ready, gently begin to bring your awareness back to your physical surroundings. Wiggle your fingers and toes, stretch your body if it feels good, and slowly open your eyes. Take a moment to savor the calm and centeredness you've cultivated during this meditation.

Remember, you can return to this garden in your mind anytime you need a moment of peace and tranquility. Carry the intention you set with you throughout your day, allowing it to guide and inspire you.

EXERCISE # 5 : CENTER YOUR BODY GUIDED MEDITATION

WHAT WERE YOU THINKING AND FEELING DURING THE MEDITATION? AND AFTERWARDS?

_____

_____

_____

_____

_____

_____

WANT TO CREATE YOUR OWN GUIDED MEDITATION? WRITE YOUR OWN HERE....

_____

_____

_____

_____

_____

_____

CHAPTER 4

〜〜〜〜〜〜〜〜

LEARNING TO BE HONEST WITH MYSELF

〜〜〜〜〜〜〜〜

Having a truly mindful moment involves letting yourself be honest and allowing yourself to feel what you feel without telling yourself that it is good or bad.

When we think or feel something and immediately attribute a good or bad feeling to it, other feelings get shoved in there, too, like guilt, shame, regret, bitterness, anger, frustration, and the list goes on.

WE NEED TO BE ABLE TO UNDERSTAND AND KNOW OURSELVES IN ORDER TO CHALLENGE OURSELVES TO BE EVEN BETTER.

After that happens, we lose the original feeling and thought that went with it. We don't get the time to experience and understand how that emotion came to be.

That doesn't mean that we should never attribute judgment to our actions, thoughts, and feelings. It only means that while we engage in mindfulness, it's important to focus on the 'raw' thoughts and emotions that we are experiencing and accept them for what they are in a calm and relaxed place. And then, after we have exited our mindfulness practice, we can think about what next steps need to happen for self-growth.

THE CHALLENGE OF
OPENING UP

Now, it can be really difficult to learn how to allow ourselves to be honest and open about what we are actually thinking and feeling. But did you know that one of the main reasons why it is difficult is because we've already decided we don't like what we are thinking and feeling? We don't trust ourselves to think things out well and in a 'good' way. And that comes from a lack of self-acceptance.

So, take the first step and repeat after me:

> "I BELIEVE THAT I HAVE THE BEST INTENTIONS FOR MYSELF AND OTHERS, AND THAT I HAVE THE STRENGTH AND RESOURCES TO THINK FAIRLY ABOUT MYSELF AND OTHERS AROUND ME, AND TO ACT WITH KINDNESS TO BOTH."

WE'VE GOT SOME GREAT TOOLS TO HELP YOU LEARN HOW TO BE MORE HONEST WITH YOURSELF AND ACCEPT YOURSELF FOR WHO YOU ARE:

1. Loads of journaling prompts
2. Activity: Write a letter to your future self and hide it away for later.

MINDFULNESS JOURNALING PROMPTS

ARE YOU READY TO GET STARTED ON YOUR JOURNEY TOWARDS SELF-ACCEPTANCE?
ARE YOU READY TO EXPRESS YOUR RAW THOUGHTS AND FEELINGS?

This journal is probably the safest place for you to get started. So, before you get further on, take this time to practice journaling using this list of prompts.

Journaling prompts are simply questions that you can ask yourself and reflect upon. Try to remember to be open and honest with yourself and give yourself room to answer these questions. All of these questions are designed to help you be centered on today and not worry about the stressors happening in your life. They are meant to help you explore who you are in detail and bring you to a state of understanding and accepting yourself.

REMEMBER, JOURNALING IS A PERSONAL AND INTROSPECTIVE PRACTICE. FEEL FREE TO ADAPT THESE PROMPTS OR ADD YOUR OWN TO SUIT YOUR UNIQUE EXPERIENCES AND NEEDS. ENJOY THE JOURNEY OF SELF-DISCOVERY AND MINDFULNESS!

LET'S GET STARTED!

EXERCISE # 6 PRACTICE WITH JOURNAL PROMPTS

INSTRUCTIONS

Begin by circling at least two journaling prompts from the list below, and then skip ahead to the blank journaling pages provided in part two and answer the questions. Remember to take your time and relax. If you are having trouble figuring out what to write, set a timer for yourself for about five minutes and challenge yourself not to stop writing [write absolutely anything] for the full five minutes. And then, after that, see if you feel more comfortable with writing.

REFLECT ON YOUR MORNING ROUTINE. DESCRIBE HOW YOU CAN INFUSE MINDFULNESS INTO YOUR MORNINGS TO SET A POSITIVE TONE FOR THE DAY.

WRITE ABOUT A MOMENT WHEN YOU FELT COMPLETELY PRESENT AND ENGAGED IN THE PRESENT MOMENT. WHAT WERE YOU DOING, AND HOW DID IT MAKE YOU FEEL?

WRITE ABOUT A TIME WHEN YOU CAUGHT YOURSELF BEING JUDGMENTAL OR CRITICAL OF YOURSELF OR OTHERS.

REFLECT ON THE IMPACT IT HAD AND EXPLORE HOW YOU CAN CULTIVATE A MORE COMPASSIONATE MINDSET.

EXPLORE YOUR EMOTIONS BY CREATING A FEELINGS WHEEL. IDENTIFY DIFFERENT EMOTIONS YOU'VE EXPERIENCED RECENTLY AND DESCRIBE THE SITUATIONS THAT TRIGGERED THEM.

WRITE A LIST OF ACTIVITIES THAT BRING YOU JOY AND MAKE YOU FEEL ALIVE. DESCRIBE HOW YOU CAN INCORPORATE MORE OF THESE ACTIVITIES INTO YOUR DAILY LIFE.

REFLECT ON YOUR RELATIONSHIPS. WRITE ABOUT THE QUALITIES YOU VALUE IN YOUR FRIENDSHIPS AND HOW YOU CAN SHOW UP MINDFULLY AND AUTHENTICALLY IN YOUR INTERACTIONS.

EXERCISE # 6 PRACTICE WITH JOURNAL PROMPTS

DESCRIBE A MOMENT WHEN YOU FELT OVERWHELMED OR STRESSED. START USING MINDFULNESS TECHNIQUES SUCH AS DEEP BREATHING OR GROUNDING EXERCISES TO FIND CALM IN THOSE MOMENTS.

DESCRIBE A PLACE IN NATURE THAT BRINGS YOU A SENSE OF CALM AND PEACE. WRITE ABOUT THE SIGHTS, SOUNDS, AND SENSATIONS YOU EXPERIENCE WHEN YOU ARE THERE.

WRITE ABOUT A CHALLENGING SITUATION YOU RECENTLY FACED. HOW DID YOU APPROACH IT WITH MINDFULNESS? WHAT DID YOU LEARN FROM THE EXPERIENCE?

LIST THREE THINGS YOU ARE GRATEFUL FOR TODAY. DIVE DEEP INTO EACH ONE AND EXPLAIN WHY THEY HOLD SIGNIFICANCE IN YOUR LIFE.

WHAT DOES SELF-COMPASSION MEAN TO YOU? WRITE A LETTER TO YOURSELF, SHOWING KINDNESS AND UNDERSTANDING DURING A DIFFICULT TIME.

CHOOSE A MEAL OR SNACK AND WRITE ABOUT THE FLAVORS, TEXTURES, AND SENSATIONS YOU NOTICE AS YOU EAT IT SLOWLY AND MINDFULLY.

WRITE A LETTER TO YOUR FUTURE SELF. DESCRIBE THE PERSON YOU ASPIRE TO BECOME, YOUR DREAMS AND GOALS, AND THE STEPS YOU CAN TAKE TO WORK TOWARDS THEM MINDFULLY. [CHECK OUT THE GUIDED ACTIVITY ON PAGE 33]

WHAT DOES SELF-CARE MEAN TO YOU? WRITE A SELF-CARE PLAN THAT INCLUDES ACTIVITIES THAT CARE FOR YOUR MIND, BODY, AND SOUL.

REFLECT ON A MISTAKE OR FAILURE YOU'VE EXPERIENCED. HOW CAN YOU APPROACH IT WITH SELF-COMPASSION AND LEARN FROM IT RATHER THAN DWELLING ON REGRET?

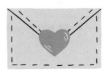

letter
to my future self

IN THIS SECTION, WRITE A LETTER TO YOUR FUTURE SELF. BUT FIRST, WE HAVE TO ANSWER THE QUESTION THAT HAS PROBABLY ALREADY POPPED UP IN YOUR MIND

why should I write a letter to my future self?

I mean, wouldn't I just be talking to myself?

WELL, YES, I GUESS SO, BUT THAT'S NOT REALLY THE POINT.
HERE ARE THREE GOOD REASONS WHY YOU SHOULD WRITE A LETTER TO YOUR FUTURE SELF:

1. IT'S FUN: WRITING A LETTER TO YOURSELF AND THEN OPENING IT YEARS LATER IS KIND OF LIKE TIME TRAVELING.
2. YOU'LL BECOME MORE SELF-AWARE: AFTER YOU WRITE OUT HOW YOU THINK AND FEEL ABOUT YOURSELF AND YOUR LIFE RIGHT NOW, YOU'LL PROBABLY LEARN A FEW THINGS ABOUT YOURSELF.
3. YOUR FUTURE SELF IS LIKELY TO BE ENCOURAGED: AFTER A FEW YEARS HAVE PASSED AND YOU OPEN THIS LETTER, A LOT OF THINGS ABOUT WHO YOU ARE, WHAT YOU THINK, AND WHAT YOU BELIEVE WILL HAVE CHANGED AND MATURED. YOU'LL HAVE A DIRECT COMPARISON OF HOW FAR YOU'VE COME.

EXERCISE # 7 LETTER TO MY FUTURE SELF

OKAY, SO NOW THAT YOU KNOW THE BENEFITS OF WRITING A LETTER TO YOUR FUTURE SELF, THIS IS HOW YOU CAN GO ABOUT IT:

FIND A QUIET SPACE

Choose a quiet and comfortable space where you can focus and reflect without distractions. This could be in your room, a cozy corner, or a peaceful outdoor setting.

SET THE MOOD

Play some soft instrumental music, light a candle, or surround yourself with items that bring you joy and comfort.

DATE THE LETTER

Start by writing the current date at the top of the page.

ADDRESS YOUR FUTURE SELF

Begin the letter by addressing your future self. You can start with "Dear Future Me" or think of a creative alternative that is meaningful to you.

REFLECT ON THE PRESENT

Take a few moments to reflect on your current state of mind, emotions, and circumstances. Consider what you're going through, your dreams, fears, and aspirations. Allow yourself to fully embrace this moment.

EXERCISE # 7 LETTER TO MY FUTURE SELF

EXPRESS YOURSELF HONESTLY

Pour out your thoughts, feelings, and dreams onto the pages. Write about your hopes, goals, and desires. Be honest and authentic in your expression, as this letter is for your eyes only.

ASK QUESTIONS

Consider questions you would like your future self to answer when you read the letter again.

CELEBRATE YOUR ACHIEVEMENTS

Acknowledge and celebrate the achievements and milestones you've reached at the time of writing. This will serve as a reminder of your progress and growth when you read the letter in the future.

OFFER YOURSELF ENCOURAGEMENT

Write words of encouragement and support to your future self. Remind her of her strengths, resilience, and ability to overcome challenges. Share any wisdom or advice you have gained so far.

END ON A HIGH NOTE

Conclude the letter with a heartfelt closing. Sign your name and add any symbols or doodles that represent who you are. Consider decorating the envelope or adding a personal touch to make it special.

EXERCISE # 7 LETTER TO MY FUTURE SELF

OKAY, SO YOU'VE WRITTEN YOUR LETTER. **NOW WHAT?**

Seal and Store the Letter:

ONCE YOU HAVE FINISHED WRITING THE LETTER, CAREFULLY FOLD IT AND SEAL IT IN AN ENVELOPE. WRITE THE DATE ON THE ENVELOPE, INDICATING WHEN YOU PLAN TO OPEN IT IN THE FUTURE. THIS WILL MAKE IT MORE MEANINGFUL AND CREATE A SENSE OF ANTICIPATION.

Choose a Safe Place:

FIND A SAFE AND SECURE PLACE TO STORE THE SEALED LETTER. IT COULD BE A SPECIAL BOX, A DRAWER, OR ANY LOCATION WHERE IT WON'T GET LOST OR DAMAGED. MAKE SURE IT'S EASILY ACCESSIBLE WHEN THE DESIGNATED TIME COMES TO OPEN IT.

Set a Reminder:

TO ENSURE YOU DON'T FORGET ABOUT THE LETTER; SET A REMINDER IN YOUR CALENDAR OR PHONE FOR THE DATE WHEN YOU PLAN TO OPEN IT. THIS WILL HELP YOU LOOK FORWARD TO THE FUTURE AND REMIND YOU OF THE COMMITMENT YOU MADE TO YOURSELF.

Continue with Self-Reflection:

USE THIS EXPERIENCE AS AN OPPORTUNITY FOR CONTINUED SELF-REFLECTION AND PERSONAL GROWTH. REGULARLY ENGAGE IN ACTIVITIES LIKE JOURNALING, MEDITATION, OR MINDFULNESS EXERCISES TO STAY CONNECTED WITH YOURSELF AND YOUR EVOLVING THOUGHTS, DREAMS, AND ASPIRATIONS.

CHAPTER 5

GRATITUDE & MINDFULNESS

PRACTICING GRATITUDE IS A VERY COMMON MINDFULNESS PRACTICE.

If you live in a household of people who love to read, chances are there will be a book or journal on someone's bookshelf that is about gratitude.

GRATITUDE IS THE QUALITY OF BEING THANKFUL; READINESS TO SHOW APPRECIATION FOR AND TO RETURN KINDNESS [oxford dictionary].

And you've probably heard of a 'gratitude practice,' which essentially means that you've made a plan with yourself to be intentional about noticing things in your life that you are grateful for.

WHAT ARE THE BENEFITS OF GRATITUDE?

Studies have shown that people who are intentional about recognizing the good things in their lives are less likely to suffer from mental health concerns, including depression, anxiety, excessive worry, and more.

You're likely to have higher energy levels, better mood regulation, better sleep quality, improved attentiveness, and more.

SO YOU MIGHT BE THINKING, "I DON'T REALLY HAVE MUCH TO BE GRATEFUL FOR..."

First of all, we are really sorry that it sounds like you're going through some rough times.

Everyone has at least one thing that they can be grateful for, no matter what their current circumstances are. Here's a short list of some simple things in your life that you could be grateful for [that you may not have thought of]:

- THE SNOOZE BUTTON ON YOUR ALARM CLOCK
- YOUR FAVORITE SHIRT THAT STILL LOOKS GOOD EVEN THOUGH IT WENT THROUGH THE HIGH HEAT CYCLE OF THE DRYER.
- THE TEACHER AT SCHOOL THAT REALLY SEEMS TO CARE AND ENCOURAGES YOU TO DO BETTER.
- YOUR BEST FRIEND WHO HAS BEEN WITH YOU THROUGH DIFFICULT TIMES IN THE PAST
- YOUR STRONG, YOUTHFUL BODY AND GOOD HEALTH
- THE FRESH AIR THAT YOU BREATHED IN DURING YOUR MORNING WALK TO SCHOOL

MINDFULNESS AND GRATITUDE GO TOGETHER LIKE SALT & PEPPER

HOW DO I COMBINE GRATITUDE WITH MY MINDFULNESS PRACTICE THAT I ALREADY STARTED?

Well, it's quite simple, really. All you have to do is save space in your journal to write about at least three things in your day that you are grateful for.

And, if you skip ahead to the blank journaling pages in this book, you'll notice at the bottom of the first page of your daily mindfulness journal, there is a space to write a few things that you're grateful for;

TODAY I AM GRATEFUL FOR:	1. 2. 3.

You can also take as much space as you want in the blank journaling pages to mention the things, people, and situations that you are grateful for today.

And remember, you don't have to have a perfect life to be grateful. Things could be going very wrong, and still, you can find something to be grateful for.

It's all about how you choose to see things...

even more

Mindfulness

activities

EXERCISE # 8 TEN MINUTES OF SILENCE

THIS WORLD IS LOUD AND BUSY. THERE IS ALWAYS SOMETHING TO DO, SOMEWHERE TO GO AND SOMEONE TO SEE.

But all that rushing around can be really stressful and tiring.
Have you ever felt like there's just too much going on in your life?
Most people have.
Here's a really simple thing you can do to de-stress and calm your
worried and busy mind:

BE SILENT

Yep, it's that simple.
Just stop talking. Take a few minutes out of your day and be
completely silent.
Intrigued? Great! If you'd like to have this silent time alone without a
guide, that is perfectly fine. But if you're not sure what you'd do
during your 10 minutes of silence, then there's a guide on the next
page.

Silence

ten minutes of SILENCE

FIND A QUIET SPACE
Choose a quiet and comfortable space where you won't be interrupted for 10 minutes. It could be your room, a cozy corner, or a peaceful outdoor spot.

SET A TIMER
Set a timer for 10 minutes to help you stay focused and committed to the practice. Use a timer on your phone or any other device that won't disrupt your silence.

GET COMFORTABLE
Find a comfortable sitting position. You can sit cross-legged on a cushion, sit on a chair with your feet planted firmly on the ground, or even lie down if that helps you relax while staying awake and alert.

CLOSE YOUR EYES
Minimize external distractions. If closing your eyes isn't ideal, soften your gaze and focus on a spot in front of you without fixating on it.

OBSERVE YOUR BREATH
Notice the natural rhythm of your breath as it flows in and out. Feel the sensations of your breath entering and leaving your body.

NOTICE YOUR THOUGHTS AND EMOTIONS
As you sit in silence, thoughts and emotions may arise. Instead of getting caught up in them, practice observing them without judgment. Acknowledge their presence and let them pass by, returning your attention to your breath.

Shh

SHHHH...

PRACTICE INNER STILLNESS

Embrace the silence and practice a sense of inner stillness. Allow your mind to settle and find a place of calm and quiet within. It's normal for thoughts to arise, but gently guide your focus back to the present moment.

ENGAGE YOUR SENSES

While sitting in silence, become aware of your senses. Notice any sounds around you—the distant hum of traffic, birds chirping, or the rustling of leaves. Feel the sensation of your body on the surface you're sitting on. Observe any scents in the air. Engage with the present moment through your senses.

PRACTICE NON-JUDGMENT

As you observe your thoughts, emotions, and sensations, practice non-judgment. Allow them to arise and pass without getting caught up in evaluating or analyzing them. Embrace a mindset of acceptance and curiosity.

CULTIVATE GRATITUDE

Use this time of silence to cultivate gratitude. Bring to mind things you appreciate and are grateful for in your life. It could be relationships, opportunities, or simple moments of joy. Allow gratitude to fill your heart and deepen your connection with the present moment.

AFTER THE SILENCE

Welcome back! You've just finished your ten minutes of silence!

HOW WAS IT?

NATURE walk

66 **Spending time outside enjoying nature has been scientifically proven to help lessen the effects of anxiety and depression.** 99

[University of Minnesota]

Nature has enormous positive benefits for our mental and physical health. And that's because there are no traffic jams in nature. There are no ugly verbal disputes. There are no signs of the overwhelming weight of your responsibilities in your regular life.

In nature, you can relax and listen to the birds. And that's where we are going. I want to encourage you to go on your nature walk.

EXERCISE # 10 NATURE WALK

BUT FIRST WE HAVE TO REMIND YOU ABOUT......

SAFETY!

Nature is not always safe. You could slip into a rushing river and lose your way on a path you thought you were familiar with or be in the wrong place at the wrong time. There are dangers lurking around every corner, so it's better to take precautions. Follow these rules when making plans to go on your nature walk:

ASK YOUR PARENT IF YOU CAN GO & TELL THEM WHEN AND WHERE YOU'RE GOING.

We know you're capable of keeping yourself safe, but it's still really important to let a parent know when you will be on your own, especially in nature. Also, be sure to let your parent know when they can expect you to be home.

KEEP YOUR PHONE ON VIBRATE.

I know this is a mindfulness exercise, but you will want to have your phone handy if something happens. So keep it on vibrate, but otherwise, don't look at it.

SAFETY IN NUMBERS: GO WITH A FRIEND.

If you choose to do this, make sure you tell your friend the reason why you want to go on the nature walk [as a mindfulness exercise].

EXERCISE # 10   NATURE WALK

GO TO A PUBLIC PLACE.

The safest place for you to go on your nature walk is a trail in a city park, where tons of other people are. You'll still be able to enjoy the nature around you, but you'll have the protection of 'the public eye.'

IF NOT A PUBLIC PLACE, THEN AT LEAST PREPARE.

If you've decided to go to a place that is a little more secluded, then at least do your research and understand the trails and the terrain. Pay attention to the reputation that this place has. [i.e., is it a known hangout for people who may be dangerous?]

BRING SOME SURVIVAL STUFF.

At the very least, you should bring a bottle of water, and if you really want to be prepared for the worst, you'll want to bring a backpack full of survival gear like healthy snacks, a sleeping bag, extra clothes, something to make a fire, etc.

LET'S walk

ARE YOU READY TO START YOUR NATURE WALK ADVENTURE?
HERE WE GO!

CHOOSE A LOCATION

Select a nearby location where you can immerse yourself in nature. It could be a local park, a hiking trail, a beach, or any natural area that appeals to you. Consider the time you have available.

CHECK THE WEATHER

Before heading out, check the weather forecast to ensure it's suitable for a nature walk. Dress appropriately for the conditions, wearing comfortable clothes and footwear. Consider bringing a hat, sunscreen, insect repellent, and a water bottle.

SLOW DOWN YOUR BRAIN

Take a few moments before you start walking to practice mindfulness. Stand still, and take a few deep breaths. Pay attention to the sounds, scents, and sensations around you. Ground yourself in the present moment.

PAY ATTENTION TO YOUR SENSES

As you begin your walk, engage your senses to fully experience nature. Notice the colors and shapes of the plants and flowers. Listen to the sounds of birds chirping, leaves rustling, or water flowing. Feel the texture of tree bark, leaves, or rocks. Take in the scents of the earth, flowers, or the ocean breeze.

PAUSE & REFLECT

Along your nature walk, find moments to pause and reflect. Sit on a bench, lean against a tree, or find a peaceful spot to simply be still. Reflect on how nature makes you feel and any insights that arise.

ENGAGE WITH NATURE

Take the opportunity to engage with nature in different ways. If allowed, touch the leaves or flowers gently. Collect small treasures like rocks or fallen leaves as keepsakes. If you're near a body of water, dip your toes in or concentrate on the soothing sounds.

APPRECIATE THE WORLD AROUND YOU

Throughout your walk, be grateful for the natural world. Express appreciation for the beauty, diversity, and calm that surrounds you.

EXERCISE # 10 NATURE WALK

SO, HOW WAS YOUR NATURE WALK? DID YOU ENJOY YOURSELF? CAN YOU TELL THAT YOUR BODY IS MORE RELAXED AND REFRESHED? THERE ARE SO MANY LESSONS TO BE LEARNED ON A NATURE WALK. LET'S UNLOCK THOSE TOGETHER.

RELAX IN A PEACEFUL SPOT OUTSIDE

After completing the nature walk, find a peaceful spot where you can sit or stand and continue to connect with nature. It could be a comfortable bench, a patch of grass, or a scenic view.

TAKE A MOMENT OF STILLNESS

Pause for a few moments and experience the stillness. Don't think about anything else. Take a deep breath and let go of any remaining distractions or thoughts from the outside world.

ENGAGE YOUR SENSES

Notice the colors, shapes, and textures around you. Observe the way the sunlight filters through the leaves or the sounds of birds chirping. Take a deep breath and savor the scents of the outdoors.

EXPRESS GRATITUDE

Take a moment to show your gratitude for the time you spent in nature. You can think of how peaceful your experience was and how beautiful the surroundings were.

REFLECT & JOURNAL

Find a quiet moment to reflect on your nature walk. Take out your journal [or just write below] and express your observations, feelings, and insights. Reflect on any significant moments or connections you experienced with nature. Use your journal as a space to capture the essence of your walk and the impact it had on you.

_____

_____

_____

_____

_____

_____

_____

_____

_____

_____

_____

CARRY NATURE'S LESSONS WITH YOU

As you prepare to end your nature walk, think about what you've learned and how you can apply that to your everyday life. And if you really enjoyed this experience, think about how you can connect with nature more often.

RETURN WITH MINDFULNESS

As you transition back to your daily routine, give it your best shot to keep that mindset with you. Be thankful for the small and beautiful things in life and find peace where you can.

My daily Mindfulness JOURNAL

[daTe]

today i'm feeling:

draw your own

today I want to be more mindful by:

- ☐ having periods of silence
- ☐ appreciating the little but beautiful things in life
- ☐ taking deep breaths, especially when I feel stressed.
- ☐ listening to others well

❋ my daily mindfulness practice: ❋

Today I _____

for _____ [how long?]

before my mindfulness routine I...

felt these emotions:

was thinking about:

tried to concentrate on:

found this difficult:

really enjoyed:

afterward, I felt _____

and I learned _____

I CHOOSE TO FEEL: AND WILL FOCUS ON:

TODAY

TODAY I AM GRATEFUL FOR:

1.

2.

3.

My daily Mindfulness JOURNAL

[daTe]

NOT SURE WHAT TO WRITE ABOUT? HERE'S A FEW IDEAS:

| 3 MOMENTS FROM TODAY THAT YOU'D LIKE TO REMEMBER | SOMETHING THAT YOU STRUGGLED WITH TODAY AND HOW YOU CAN GROW TOMORROW | YOUR THOUGHTS AND FEELINGS ABOUT YOUR MINDFULNESS ROUTINE |

HERE'S A TIP: THERE ARE ALSO A WHOLE BUNCH OF JOURNALING PROMPTS ON PAGES 40-41. CHECK THOSE OUT!

My daily Mindfulness JOURNAL

[date] _____

today i'm feeling:

draw your own

today I want to be more mindful by:

- ☐ having periods of silence
- ☐ appreciating the little but beautiful things in life
- ☐ taking deep breaths, especially when I feel stressed.
- ☐ listening to others well

❄ my daily mindfulness practice: ❄

Today I _____

for _____ [how long?]

before my mindfulness routine I...

felt these emotions:

was thinking about:

tried to concentrate on:

found this difficult:

really enjoyed:

afterward, I felt _____

and I learned _____

I CHOOSE TO FEEL: AND WILL FOCUS ON:

TODAY

TODAY I AM GRATEFUL FOR:

1.
2.
3.

My daily Mindfulness JOURNAL

NOT SURE WHAT TO WRITE ABOUT? HERE'S A FEW IDEAS:

3 MOMENTS FROM TODAY THAT YOU'D LIKE TO REMEMBER	SOMETHING THAT YOU STRUGGLED WITH TODAY AND HOW YOU CAN GROW TOMORROW	YOUR THOUGHTS AND FEELINGS ABOUT YOUR MINDFULNESS ROUTINE

_____

_____

_____

_____

_____

_____

_____

_____

_____

HERE'S A TIP: THERE ARE ALSO A WHOLE BUNCH OF JOURNALING PROMPTS ON PAGES 40-41. CHECK THOSE OUT!

My daily Mindfulness JOURNAL

today i'm feeling:

draw your own

today I want to be more mindful by:

☐ having periods of silence

☐ appreciating the little but beautiful things in life

☐ taking deep breaths, especially when I feel stressed.

☐ listening to others well

❋ my daily mindfulness practice: ❋

Today I _____

for _____ [how long?]

before my mindfulness routine I...

felt these emotions:

was thinking about:

tried to concentrate on:

found this difficult:

really enjoyed:

afterward, I felt _____

and I learned _____

I CHOOSE TO FEEL: AND WILL FOCUS ON:

TODAY

TODAY I AM GRATEFUL FOR:

1.
2.
3.

My daily Mindfulness JOURNAL

[daTe]

NOT SURE WHAT TO WRITE ABOUT? HERE'S A FEW IDEAS:

3 MOMENTS FROM TODAY THAT YOU'D LIKE TO REMEMBER	SOMETHING THAT YOU STRUGGLED WITH TODAY AND HOW YOU CAN GROW TOMORROW	YOUR THOUGHTS AND FEELINGS ABOUT YOUR MINDFULNESS ROUTINE

HERE'S A TIP: THERE ARE ALSO A WHOLE BUNCH OF JOURNALING PROMPTS ON PAGES 40-41. CHECK THOSE OUT!

My daily Mindfulness JOURNAL

[daTe] _____

today i'm feeling:

draw your own

today I want to be more mindful by:

- [ ] having periods of silence
- [ ] appreciating the little but beautiful things in life
- [ ] taking deep breaths, especially when I feel stressed.
- [ ] listening to others well

❋ my daily mindfulness practice: ❋

Today I _____

for _____ [how long?]

before my mindfulness routine I...

felt these emotions:

was thinking about:

tried to concentrate on:

found this difficult:

really enjoyed:

afterward, I felt _____

and I learned _____

I CHOOSE TO FEEL: AND WILL FOCUS ON:

TODAY

TODAY I AM GRATEFUL FOR:

1.

2.

3.

My daily Mindfulness JOURNAL

[daTe]

NOT SURE WHAT TO WRITE ABOUT? HERE'S A FEW IDEAS:

3 MOMENTS FROM TODAY THAT YOU'D LIKE TO REMEMBER

SOMETHING THAT YOU STRUGGLED WITH TODAY AND HOW YOU CAN GROW TOMORROW

YOUR THOUGHTS AND FEELINGS ABOUT YOUR MINDFULNESS ROUTINE

HERE'S A TIP: THERE ARE ALSO A WHOLE BUNCH OF JOURNALING PROMPTS ON PAGES 40-41. CHECK THOSE OUT!

My daily Mindfulness JOURNAL

[daTe]

today i'm feeling:

draw your own

today I want to be more mindful by:

- ☐ having periods of silence
- ☐ appreciating the little but beautiful things in life
- ☐ taking deep breaths, especially when I feel stressed.
- ☐ listening to others well

❋ my daily mindfulness practice: ❋

Today I _____

for _____ [how long?]

before my mindfulness routine I...

felt these emotions:

was thinking about:

tried to concentrate on:

found this difficult:

really enjoyed:

afterward, I felt _____

and I learned _____

I CHOOSE TO FEEL: AND WILL FOCUS ON:

TODAY

TODAY I AM GRATEFUL FOR:

1.
2.
3.

My daily Mindfulness JOURNAL

NOT SURE WHAT TO WRITE ABOUT? HERE'S A FEW IDEAS:

3 MOMENTS FROM TODAY THAT YOU'D LIKE TO REMEMBER

SOMETHING THAT YOU STRUGGLED WITH TODAY AND HOW YOU CAN GROW TOMORROW

YOUR THOUGHTS AND FEELINGS ABOUT YOUR MINDFULNESS ROUTINE

HERE'S A TIP: THERE ARE ALSO A WHOLE BUNCH OF JOURNALING PROMPTS ON PAGES 40-41. CHECK THOSE OUT!

My daily Mindfulness JOURNAL

today i'm feeling:

draw your own

today I want to be more mindful by:

- ☐ having periods of silence
- ☐ appreciating the little but beautiful things in life
- ☐ taking deep breaths, especially when I feel stressed.
- ☐ listening to others well

✳ my daily mindfulness practice: ✳

Today I _____

for _____ [how long?]

before my mindfulness routine I...

felt these emotions:

was thinking about:

tried to concentrate on:

found this difficult:

really enjoyed:

afterward, I felt _____

and I learned _____

I CHOOSE TO FEEL: AND WILL FOCUS ON:

TODAY

TODAY I AM
GRATEFUL
FOR:

1.

2.

3.

My daily Mindfulness
JOURNAL

[date]

NOT SURE WHAT TO WRITE ABOUT? HERE'S A FEW IDEAS:

3 MOMENTS FROM TODAY THAT YOU'D LIKE TO REMEMBER	SOMETHING THAT YOU STRUGGLED WITH TODAY AND HOW YOU CAN GROW TOMORROW	YOUR THOUGHTS AND FEELINGS ABOUT YOUR MINDFULNESS ROUTINE

_____

_____

_____

_____

_____

_____

_____

_____

_____

HERE'S A TIP: THERE ARE ALSO A WHOLE BUNCH OF JOURNALING PROMPTS ON PAGES 40-41. CHECK THOSE OUT!

My daily Mindfulness JOURNAL

today i'm feeling:

draw your own

today I want to be more mindful by:

- ☐ having periods of silence
- ☐ appreciating the little but beautiful things in life
- ☐ taking deep breaths, especially when I feel stressed.
- ☐ listening to others well

✳ my daily mindfulness practice: ✳

Today I _____

for _____ [how long?]

before my mindfulness routine I...

felt these emotions:

was thinking about:

tried to concentrate on:

found this difficult:

really enjoyed:

afterward, I felt _____

and I learned _____

I CHOOSE TO FEEL: AND WILL FOCUS ON:

TODAY

TODAY I AM
GRATEFUL
FOR:

1.
2.
3.

My daily Mindfulness JOURNAL

NOT SURE WHAT TO WRITE ABOUT? HERE'S A FEW IDEAS:

| 3 MOMENTS FROM TODAY THAT YOU'D LIKE TO REMEMBER | SOMETHING THAT YOU STRUGGLED WITH TODAY AND HOW YOU CAN GROW TOMORROW | YOUR THOUGHTS AND FEELINGS ABOUT YOUR MINDFULNESS ROUTINE |

_____

_____

_____

_____

_____

_____

_____

_____

_____

HERE'S A TIP: THERE ARE ALSO A WHOLE BUNCH OF JOURNALING PROMPTS ON PAGES 40-41. CHECK THOSE OUT!

My daily Mindfulness JOURNAL

[date] _____

today i'm feeling:

draw your own

today I want to be more mindful by:

- ☐ having periods of silence
- ☐ appreciating the little but beautiful things in life
- ☐ taking deep breaths, especially when I feel stressed.
- ☐ listening to others well

✽ my daily mindfulness practice: ✽

Today I _____

for _____ [how long?]

before my mindfulness routine I...

felt these emotions:

was thinking about:

tried to concentrate on:

found this difficult:

really enjoyed:

afterward, I felt _____

and I learned _____

I CHOOSE TO FEEL: AND WILL FOCUS ON:

TODAY

TODAY I AM
GRATEFUL
FOR:
1.
2.
3.

My daily Mindfulness
JOURNAL

[date]

NOT SURE WHAT TO WRITE ABOUT? HERE'S A FEW IDEAS:

3 MOMENTS FROM TODAY THAT YOU'D LIKE TO REMEMBER

SOMETHING THAT YOU STRUGGLED WITH TODAY AND HOW YOU CAN GROW TOMORROW

YOUR THOUGHTS AND FEELINGS ABOUT YOUR MINDFULNESS ROUTINE

HERE'S A TIP: THERE ARE ALSO A WHOLE BUNCH OF JOURNALING PROMPTS ON PAGES 40-41. CHECK THOSE OUT!

My daily Mindfulness JOURNAL

_______ [date]

today i'm feeling:

draw your own

today I want to be more mindful by:

- ☐ having periods of silence
- ☐ appreciating the little but beautiful things in life
- ☐ taking deep breaths, especially when I feel stressed.
- ☐ listening to others well

my daily mindfulness practice:

Today I ____________

for ________ [how long?]

before my mindfulness routine I...

felt these emotions:

was thinking about:

tried to concentrate on:

found this difficult:

really enjoyed:

afterward, I felt ________

and I learned ________

I CHOOSE TO FEEL: AND WILL FOCUS ON:

TODAY

TODAY I AM GRATEFUL FOR:

1.
2.
3.

NOT SURE WHAT TO WRITE ABOUT? HERE'S A FEW IDEAS:

3 MOMENTS FROM TODAY THAT YOU'D LIKE TO REMEMBER

SOMETHING THAT YOU STRUGGLED WITH TODAY AND HOW YOU CAN GROW TOMORROW

YOUR THOUGHTS AND FEELINGS ABOUT YOUR MINDFULNESS ROUTINE

HERE'S A TIP: THERE ARE ALSO A WHOLE BUNCH OF JOURNALING PROMPTS ON PAGES 40-41. CHECK THOSE OUT!

My daily Mindfulness JOURNAL

today i'm feeling:

draw your own

today I want to be more mindful by:

- ☐ having periods of silence
- ☐ appreciating the little but beautiful things in life
- ☐ taking deep breaths, especially when I feel stressed.
- ☐ listening to others well

✳ my daily mindfulness practice: ✳

Today I _____

for _____ [how long?]

before my mindfulness routine I...

felt these emotions:

was thinking about:

tried to concentrate on:

found this difficult:

really enjoyed:

afterward, I felt _____

and I learned _____

I CHOOSE TO FEEL: AND WILL FOCUS ON:

TODAY

TODAY I AM
GRATEFUL
FOR:
1.
2.
3.

My daily Mindfulness JOURNAL

NOT SURE WHAT TO WRITE ABOUT? HERE'S A FEW IDEAS:

3 MOMENTS FROM TODAY THAT YOU'D LIKE TO REMEMBER	SOMETHING THAT YOU STRUGGLED WITH TODAY AND HOW YOU CAN GROW TOMORROW	YOUR THOUGHTS AND FEELINGS ABOUT YOUR MINDFULNESS ROUTINE

_____

_____

_____

_____

_____

_____

_____

_____

_____

HERE'S A TIP: THERE ARE ALSO A WHOLE BUNCH OF JOURNALING PROMPTS ON PAGES 40-41. CHECK THOSE OUT!

My daily Mindfulness JOURNAL

[daTe] _____

today i'm feeling:

draw your own

today I want to be more mindful by:

- ☐ having periods of silence
- ☐ appreciating the little but beautiful things in life
- ☐ taking deep breaths, especially when I feel stressed.
- ☐ listening to others well

❋ my daily mindfulness practice: ❋

Today I _____

for _____ [how long?]

before my mindfulness routine I...

felt these emotions:

was thinking about:

tried to concentrate on:

found this difficult:

really enjoyed:

afterward, I felt _____

and I learned _____

I CHOOSE TO FEEL: AND WILL FOCUS ON:

TODAY

TODAY I AM GRATEFUL FOR:

1.
2.
3.

My daily Mindfulness
JOURNAL

NOT SURE WHAT TO WRITE ABOUT? HERE'S A FEW IDEAS:

| 3 MOMENTS FROM TODAY THAT YOU'D LIKE TO REMEMBER | SOMETHING THAT YOU STRUGGLED WITH TODAY AND HOW YOU CAN GROW TOMORROW | YOUR THOUGHTS AND FEELINGS ABOUT YOUR MINDFULNESS ROUTINE |

_____

_____

_____

_____

_____

_____

_____

_____

_____

HERE'S A TIP: THERE ARE ALSO A WHOLE BUNCH OF JOURNALING PROMPTS ON PAGES 40-41. CHECK THOSE OUT!

My daily Mindfulness JOURNAL

today i'm feeling:

draw your own

today I want to be more mindful by:

- ☐ having periods of silence
- ☐ appreciating the little but beautiful things in life
- ☐ taking deep breaths, especially when I feel stressed.
- ☐ listening to others well

❋ my daily mindfulness practice: ❋

Today I _____

for _____ [how long?]

before my mindfulness routine I...

felt these emotions:

was thinking about:

tried to concentrate on:

found this difficult:

really enjoyed:

afterward, I felt _____

and I learned _____

I CHOOSE TO FEEL: AND WILL FOCUS ON:

TODAY

TODAY I AM GRATEFUL FOR:

1.

2.

3.

My daily Mindfulness
JOURNAL

NOT SURE WHAT TO WRITE ABOUT? HERE'S A FEW IDEAS:

3 MOMENTS FROM TODAY THAT YOU'D LIKE TO REMEMBER

SOMETHING THAT YOU STRUGGLED WITH TODAY AND HOW YOU CAN GROW TOMORROW

YOUR THOUGHTS AND FEELINGS ABOUT YOUR MINDFULNESS ROUTINE

_____

_____

_____

_____

_____

_____

_____

_____

HERE'S A TIP: THERE ARE ALSO A WHOLE BUNCH OF JOURNALING PROMPTS ON PAGES 40-41. CHECK THOSE OUT!

My daily Mindfulness JOURNAL

today i'm feeling:

draw your own

today I want to be more mindful by:

- ☐ having periods of silence
- ☐ appreciating the little but beautiful things in life
- ☐ taking deep breaths, especially when I feel stressed.
- ☐ listening to others well

✾ my daily mindfulness practice: ✾

Today I _____

for _____ [how long?]

before my mindfulness routine I...

felt these emotions:

was thinking about:

tried to concentrate on:

found this difficult:

really enjoyed:

afterward, I felt _____

and I learned _____

I CHOOSE TO FEEL: AND WILL FOCUS ON:

TODAY

TODAY I AM
GRATEFUL
FOR:

1.

2.

3.

My daily Mindfulness JOURNAL

[date]

NOT SURE WHAT TO WRITE ABOUT? HERE'S A FEW IDEAS:

3 MOMENTS FROM TODAY THAT YOU'D LIKE TO REMEMBER

SOMETHING THAT YOU STRUGGLED WITH TODAY AND HOW YOU CAN GROW TOMORROW

YOUR THOUGHTS AND FEELINGS ABOUT YOUR MINDFULNESS ROUTINE

HERE'S A TIP: THERE ARE ALSO A WHOLE BUNCH OF JOURNALING PROMPTS ON PAGES 40-41. CHECK THOSE OUT!

My daily Mindfulness JOURNAL

______ [daTe]

today i'm feeling:

draw your own

today I want to be more mindful by:

- [ ] having periods of silence
- [ ] appreciating the little but beautiful things in life
- [ ] taking deep breaths, especially when I feel stressed.
- [ ] listening to others well

my daily mindfulness practice:

Today I ______

for ______ [how long?]

before my mindfulness routine I...

felt these emotions:

was thinking about:

tried to concentrate on:

found this difficult:

really enjoyed:

afterward, I felt ______

and I learned ______

TODAY

I CHOOSE TO FEEL:

AND WILL FOCUS ON:

TODAY I AM GRATEFUL FOR:

1.
2.
3.

My daily Mindfulness JOURNAL

NOT SURE WHAT TO WRITE ABOUT? HERE'S A FEW IDEAS:

3 MOMENTS FROM TODAY THAT YOU'D LIKE TO REMEMBER	SOMETHING THAT YOU STRUGGLED WITH TODAY AND HOW YOU CAN GROW TOMORROW	YOUR THOUGHTS AND FEELINGS ABOUT YOUR MINDFULNESS ROUTINE

_____

_____

_____

_____

_____

_____

_____

_____

_____

HERE'S A TIP: THERE ARE ALSO A WHOLE BUNCH OF JOURNALING PROMPTS ON PAGES 40-41. CHECK THOSE OUT!

My daily Mindfulness JOURNAL

today i'm feeling:

draw your own

today I want to be more mindful by:

- ☐ having periods of silence
- ☐ appreciating the little but beautiful things in life
- ☐ taking deep breaths, especially when I feel stressed.
- ☐ listening to others well

❋ my daily mindfulness practice: ❋

Today I _____

for _____ [how long?]

before my mindfulness routine I...

felt these emotions:

was thinking about:

tried to concentrate on:

found this difficult:

really enjoyed:

afterward, I felt _____

and I learned _____

I CHOOSE TO FEEL: AND WILL FOCUS ON:

TODAY

TODAY I AM
GRATEFUL
FOR:

1.
2.
3.

My daily Mindfulness
JOURNAL

NOT SURE WHAT TO WRITE ABOUT? HERE'S A FEW IDEAS:

3 MOMENTS FROM TODAY THAT YOU'D LIKE TO REMEMBER

SOMETHING THAT YOU STRUGGLED WITH TODAY AND HOW YOU CAN GROW TOMORROW

YOUR THOUGHTS AND FEELINGS ABOUT YOUR MINDFULNESS ROUTINE

_____

_____

_____

_____

_____

_____

_____

_____

_____

HERE'S A TIP: THERE ARE ALSO A WHOLE BUNCH OF JOURNALING PROMPTS ON PAGES 40-41. CHECK THOSE OUT!

My daily Mindfulness JOURNAL

[date] _____

today i'm feeling:

draw your own

today I want to be more mindful by:

- ☐ having periods of silence
- ☐ appreciating the little but beautiful things in life
- ☐ taking deep breaths, especially when I feel stressed.
- ☐ listening to others well

❋ my daily mindfulness practice: ❋

Today I _____

for _____ [how long?]

before my mindfulness routine I...

felt these emotions:

was thinking about:

tried to concentrate on:

found this difficult:

really enjoyed:

afterward, I felt _____

and I learned _____

I CHOOSE TO FEEL: AND WILL FOCUS ON:

TODAY

TODAY I AM
GRATEFUL
FOR:

1.
2.
3.

My daily Mindfulness JOURNAL

[daTe]

NOT SURE WHAT TO WRITE ABOUT? HERE'S A FEW IDEAS:

| 3 MOMENTS FROM TODAY THAT YOU'D LIKE TO REMEMBER | SOMETHING THAT YOU STRUGGLED WITH TODAY AND HOW YOU CAN GROW TOMORROW | YOUR THOUGHTS AND FEELINGS ABOUT YOUR MINDFULNESS ROUTINE |

_____

_____

_____

_____

_____

_____

_____

_____

HERE'S A TIP: THERE ARE ALSO A WHOLE BUNCH OF JOURNALING PROMPTS ON PAGES 40-41. CHECK THOSE OUT!

My daily Mindfulness JOURNAL

today i'm feeling:

draw your own

today I want to be more mindful by:

- ☐ having periods of silence
- ☐ appreciating the little but beautiful things in life
- ☐ taking deep breaths, especially when I feel stressed.
- ☐ listening to others well

❋ my daily mindfulness practice: ❋

Today I _____

for _____ [how long?]

before my mindfulness routine I...

felt these emotions:

was thinking about:

tried to concentrate on:

found this difficult:

really enjoyed:

afterward, I felt _____

and I learned _____

I CHOOSE TO FEEL: AND WILL FOCUS ON:

TODAY

TODAY I AM
GRATEFUL
FOR:

1.

2.

3.

My daily Mindfulness
JOURNAL

NOT SURE WHAT TO WRITE ABOUT? HERE'S A FEW IDEAS:

| 3 MOMENTS FROM TODAY THAT YOU'D LIKE TO REMEMBER | SOMETHING THAT YOU STRUGGLED WITH TODAY AND HOW YOU CAN GROW TOMORROW | YOUR THOUGHTS AND FEELINGS ABOUT YOUR MINDFULNESS ROUTINE |

_____

_____

_____

_____

_____

_____

_____

_____

_____

HERE'S A TIP: THERE ARE ALSO A WHOLE BUNCH OF JOURNALING PROMPTS ON PAGES 40-41. CHECK THOSE OUT!

My daily Mindfulness JOURNAL

[date] _____

today i'm feeling:

draw your own

today I want to be more mindful by:

- ☐ having periods of silence
- ☐ appreciating the little but beautiful things in life
- ☐ taking deep breaths, especially when I feel stressed.
- ☐ listening to others well

✾ my daily mindfulness practice: ✾

Today I _____

for _____ [how long?]

before my mindfulness routine I...

felt these emotions:

was thinking about:

tried to concentrate on:

found this difficult:

really enjoyed:

afterward, I felt _____

and I learned _____

I CHOOSE TO FEEL: AND WILL FOCUS ON:

TODAY

TODAY I AM GRATEFUL FOR:

1.

2.

3.

My daily Mindfulness JOURNAL

NOT SURE WHAT TO WRITE ABOUT? HERE'S A FEW IDEAS:

3 MOMENTS FROM TODAY THAT YOU'D LIKE TO REMEMBER	SOMETHING THAT YOU STRUGGLED WITH TODAY AND HOW YOU CAN GROW TOMORROW	YOUR THOUGHTS AND FEELINGS ABOUT YOUR MINDFULNESS ROUTINE

HERE'S A TIP: THERE ARE ALSO A WHOLE BUNCH OF JOURNALING PROMPTS ON PAGES 40-41. CHECK THOSE OUT!

My daily Mindfulness JOURNAL

[daTe]

today i'm feeling:

draw your own

today I want to be more mindful by:

- ☐ having periods of silence
- ☐ appreciating the little but beautiful things in life
- ☐ taking deep breaths, especially when I feel stressed.
- ☐ listening to others well

❊ my daily mindfulness practice: ❊

Today I _____

for _____ [how long?]

before my mindfulness routine I...

felt these emotions:

was thinking about:

tried to concentrate on:

found this difficult:

really enjoyed:

afterward, I felt _____

and I learned _____

I CHOOSE TO FEEL: AND WILL FOCUS ON:

TODAY

TODAY I AM GRATEFUL FOR:

1.
2.
3.

My daily Mindfulness JOURNAL

[date]

NOT SURE WHAT TO WRITE ABOUT? HERE'S A FEW IDEAS:

| 3 MOMENTS FROM TODAY THAT YOU'D LIKE TO REMEMBER | SOMETHING THAT YOU STRUGGLED WITH TODAY AND HOW YOU CAN GROW TOMORROW | YOUR THOUGHTS AND FEELINGS ABOUT YOUR MINDFULNESS ROUTINE |

HERE'S A TIP: THERE ARE ALSO A WHOLE BUNCH OF JOURNALING PROMPTS ON PAGES 40-41. CHECK THOSE OUT!

My daily Mindfulness JOURNAL

today i'm feeling:

draw your own

today I want to be more mindful by:

- [ ] having periods of silence
- [ ] appreciating the little but beautiful things in life
- [ ] taking deep breaths, especially when I feel stressed.
- [ ] listening to others well

❋ my daily mindfulness practice: ❋

Today I _____

for _____ [how long?]

before my mindfulness routine I...

felt these emotions:

was thinking about:

tried to concentrate on:

found this difficult:

really enjoyed:

afterward, I felt _____

and I learned _____

I CHOOSE TO FEEL: AND WILL FOCUS ON:

TODAY

TODAY I AM GRATEFUL FOR:

1.

2.

3.

My daily Mindfulness JOURNAL

[daTe]

NOT SURE WHAT TO WRITE ABOUT? HERE'S A FEW IDEAS:

3 MOMENTS FROM TODAY THAT YOU'D LIKE TO REMEMBER

SOMETHING THAT YOU STRUGGLED WITH TODAY AND HOW YOU CAN GROW TOMORROW

YOUR THOUGHTS AND FEELINGS ABOUT YOUR MINDFULNESS ROUTINE

HERE'S A TIP: THERE ARE ALSO A WHOLE BUNCH OF JOURNALING PROMPTS ON PAGES 40-41. CHECK THOSE OUT!

My daily Mindfulness JOURNAL

today i'm feeling:

draw your own

today I want to be more mindful by:

☐ having periods of silence

☐ appreciating the little but beautiful things in life

☐ taking deep breaths, especially when I feel stressed.

☐ listening to others well

❋ my daily mindfulness practice: ❋

Today I _____

for _____ [how long?]

before my mindfulness routine I...

felt these emotions:

was thinking about:

tried to concentrate on:

found this difficult:

really enjoyed:

afterward, I felt _____

and I learned _____

I CHOOSE TO FEEL: AND WILL FOCUS ON:

TODAY

TODAY I AM
GRATEFUL
FOR:

1.

2.

3.

My daily Mindfulness
JOURNAL

NOT SURE WHAT TO WRITE ABOUT? HERE'S A FEW IDEAS:

3 MOMENTS FROM TODAY THAT YOU'D LIKE TO REMEMBER

SOMETHING THAT YOU STRUGGLED WITH TODAY AND HOW YOU CAN GROW TOMORROW

YOUR THOUGHTS AND FEELINGS ABOUT YOUR MINDFULNESS ROUTINE

HERE'S A TIP: THERE ARE ALSO A WHOLE BUNCH OF JOURNALING PROMPTS ON PAGES 40-41. CHECK THOSE OUT!

My daily Mindfulness JOURNAL

[date] _____

today i'm feeling:

draw your own

today I want to be more mindful by:

- [ ] having periods of silence
- [ ] appreciating the little but beautiful things in life
- [ ] taking deep breaths, especially when I feel stressed.
- [ ] listening to others well

❊ my daily mindfulness practice: ❊

Today I _____

for _____ [how long?]

before my mindfulness routine I...

felt these emotions:

was thinking about:

tried to concentrate on:

found this difficult:

really enjoyed:

afterward, I felt _____

and I learned _____

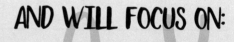

I CHOOSE TO FEEL: AND WILL FOCUS ON:

TODAY

TODAY I AM
GRATEFUL
FOR:

1.

2.

3.

My daily Mindfulness JOURNAL

[daTe]

NOT SURE WHAT TO WRITE ABOUT? HERE'S A FEW IDEAS:

| 3 MOMENTS FROM TODAY THAT YOU'D LIKE TO REMEMBER | SOMETHING THAT YOU STRUGGLED WITH TODAY AND HOW YOU CAN GROW TOMORROW | YOUR THOUGHTS AND FEELINGS ABOUT YOUR MINDFULNESS ROUTINE |

_____

_____

_____

_____

_____

_____

_____

_____

_____

HERE'S A TIP: THERE ARE ALSO A WHOLE BUNCH OF JOURNALING PROMPTS ON PAGES 40-41. CHECK THOSE OUT!

My daily Mindfulness JOURNAL

today i'm feeling:

draw your own

today I want to be more mindful by:

☐ having periods of silence

☐ appreciating the little but beautiful things in life

☐ taking deep breaths, especially when I feel stressed.

☐ listening to others well

❋ my daily mindfulness practice: ❋

Today I _____

for _____ [how long?]

before my mindfulness routine I...

felt these emotions:

was thinking about:

tried to concentrate on:

found this difficult:

really enjoyed:

afterward, I felt _____

and I learned _____

I CHOOSE TO FEEL: AND WILL FOCUS ON:

TODAY

TODAY I AM
GRATEFUL
FOR:

1.

2.

3.

My daily Mindfulness JOURNAL

[daTe]

NOT SURE WHAT TO WRITE ABOUT? HERE'S A FEW IDEAS:

3 MOMENTS FROM TODAY THAT YOU'D LIKE TO REMEMBER

SOMETHING THAT YOU STRUGGLED WITH TODAY AND HOW YOU CAN GROW TOMORROW

YOUR THOUGHTS AND FEELINGS ABOUT YOUR MINDFULNESS ROUTINE

HERE'S A TIP: THERE ARE ALSO A WHOLE BUNCH OF JOURNALING PROMPTS ON PAGES 40-41. CHECK THOSE OUT!

My daily Mindfulness JOURNAL

today i'm feeling:

draw your own

today I want to be more mindful by:

☐ having periods of silence

☐ appreciating the little but beautiful things in life

☐ taking deep breaths, especially when I feel stressed.

☐ listening to others well

❋ my daily mindfulness practice: ❋

Today I _____

for _____ [how long?]

before my mindfulness routine I...

felt these emotions:

was thinking about:

tried to concentrate on:

found this difficult:

really enjoyed:

afterward, I felt _____

and I learned _____

I CHOOSE TO FEEL: AND WILL FOCUS ON:

TODAY

TODAY I AM GRATEFUL FOR:

1.

2.

3.

My daily Mindfulness JOURNAL

[daTe]

NOT SURE WHAT TO WRITE ABOUT? HERE'S A FEW IDEAS:

3 MOMENTS FROM TODAY THAT YOU'D LIKE TO REMEMBER	SOMETHING THAT YOU STRUGGLED WITH TODAY AND HOW YOU CAN GROW TOMORROW	YOUR THOUGHTS AND FEELINGS ABOUT YOUR MINDFULNESS ROUTINE

HERE'S A TIP: THERE ARE ALSO A WHOLE BUNCH OF JOURNALING PROMPTS ON PAGES 40-41. CHECK THOSE OUT!

My daily Mindfulness JOURNAL

[daTe] _____

today i'm feeling:

draw your own

today I want to be more mindful by:

- ☐ having periods of silence
- ☐ appreciating the little but beautiful things in life
- ☐ taking deep breaths, especially when I feel stressed.
- ☐ listening to others well

✿ my daily mindfulness practice: ✿

Today I _____

for _____ [how long?]

before my mindfulness routine I...

felt these emotions:

was thinking about:

tried to concentrate on:

found this difficult:

really enjoyed:

afterward, I felt _____

and I learned _____

I CHOOSE TO FEEL: AND WILL FOCUS ON:

T O D A Y

TODAY I AM
GRATEFUL
FOR:

1.

2.

3.

My daily Mindfulness
JOURNAL

NOT SURE WHAT TO WRITE ABOUT? HERE'S A FEW IDEAS:

| 3 MOMENTS FROM TODAY THAT YOU'D LIKE TO REMEMBER | SOMETHING THAT YOU STRUGGLED WITH TODAY AND HOW YOU CAN GROW TOMORROW | YOUR THOUGHTS AND FEELINGS ABOUT YOUR MINDFULNESS ROUTINE |

_____

_____

_____

_____

_____

_____

_____

_____

HERE'S A TIP: THERE ARE ALSO A WHOLE BUNCH OF JOURNALING PROMPTS ON PAGES 40-41. CHECK THOSE OUT!

[daTe] _____

today i'm feeling:

draw your own

today I want to be more mindful by:

- [ ] having periods of silence
- [ ] appreciating the little but beautiful things in life
- [ ] taking deep breaths, especially when I feel stressed.
- [ ] listening to others well

✺ my daily mindfulness practice: ✺

Today I _____

for _____ [how long?]

before my mindfulness routine I...

felt these emotions:

was thinking about:

tried to concentrate on:

found this difficult:

really enjoyed:

afterward, I felt _____

and I learned _____

I CHOOSE TO FEEL: AND WILL FOCUS ON:

TODAY

TODAY I AM
GRATEFUL
FOR:
1.
2.
3.

My daily Mindfulness
JOURNAL

[date]

NOT SURE WHAT TO WRITE ABOUT? HERE'S A FEW IDEAS:

| 3 MOMENTS FROM TODAY THAT YOU'D LIKE TO REMEMBER | SOMETHING THAT YOU STRUGGLED WITH TODAY AND HOW YOU CAN GROW TOMORROW | YOUR THOUGHTS AND FEELINGS ABOUT YOUR MINDFULNESS ROUTINE |

_____

_____

_____

_____

_____

_____

_____

_____

HERE'S A TIP: THERE ARE ALSO A WHOLE BUNCH OF JOURNALING PROMPTS ON PAGES 40-41. CHECK THOSE OUT!

My daily Mindfulness JOURNAL

today i'm feeling:

draw your own

today I want to be more mindful by:

- ☐ having periods of silence
- ☐ appreciating the little but beautiful things in life
- ☐ taking deep breaths, especially when I feel stressed.
- ☐ listening to others well

❋ my daily mindfulness practice: ❋

Today I _____

for _____ [how long?]

before my mindfulness routine I...

felt these emotions:

was thinking about:

tried to concentrate on:

found this difficult:

really enjoyed:

afterward, I felt _____

and I learned _____

I CHOOSE TO FEEL: AND WILL FOCUS ON:

TODAY

TODAY I AM GRATEFUL FOR:
1.
2.
3.

My daily Mindfulness
JOURNAL

[date]

NOT SURE WHAT TO WRITE ABOUT? HERE'S A FEW IDEAS:

3 MOMENTS FROM TODAY THAT YOU'D LIKE TO REMEMBER

SOMETHING THAT YOU STRUGGLED WITH TODAY AND HOW YOU CAN GROW TOMORROW

YOUR THOUGHTS AND FEELINGS ABOUT YOUR MINDFULNESS ROUTINE

HERE'S A TIP: THERE ARE ALSO A WHOLE BUNCH OF JOURNALING PROMPTS ON PAGES 40-41. CHECK THOSE OUT!

My daily Mindfulness JOURNAL

today i'm feeling:

draw your own

today I want to be more mindful by:

- ☐ having periods of silence
- ☐ appreciating the little but beautiful things in life
- ☐ taking deep breaths, especially when I feel stressed.
- ☐ listening to others well

❁ my daily mindfulness practice: ❁

Today I _____

for _____ [how long?]

before my mindfulness routine I...

felt these emotions:

was thinking about:

tried to concentrate on:

found this difficult:

really enjoyed:

afterward, I felt _____

and I learned _____

I CHOOSE TO FEEL: AND WILL FOCUS ON:

TODAY

TODAY I AM
GRATEFUL
FOR:

1.

2.

3.

My daily Mindfulness
JOURNAL

_____ [date]

NOT SURE WHAT TO WRITE ABOUT? HERE'S A FEW IDEAS:

3 MOMENTS FROM TODAY THAT YOU'D LIKE TO REMEMBER

SOMETHING THAT YOU STRUGGLED WITH TODAY AND HOW YOU CAN GROW TOMORROW

YOUR THOUGHTS AND FEELINGS ABOUT YOUR MINDFULNESS ROUTINE

_____

_____

_____

_____

_____

_____

_____

_____

HERE'S A TIP: THERE ARE ALSO A WHOLE BUNCH OF JOURNALING PROMPTS ON PAGES 40-41. CHECK THOSE OUT!

My daily Mindfulness JOURNAL

[daTe]

today i'm feeling:

draw your own

today I want to be more mindful by:

- ☐ having periods of silence
- ☐ appreciating the little but beautiful things in life
- ☐ taking deep breaths, especially when I feel stressed.
- ☐ listening to others well

❋ my daily mindfulness practice: ❋

Today I _____

for _____ [how long?]

before my mindfulness routine I...

felt these emotions:

was thinking about:

tried to concentrate on:

found this difficult:

really enjoyed:

afterward, I felt _____

and I learned _____

I CHOOSE TO FEEL: AND WILL FOCUS ON:

TODAY

TODAY I AM GRATEFUL FOR:

1.

2.

3.

My daily Mindfulness
JOURNAL

[date]

NOT SURE WHAT TO WRITE ABOUT? HERE'S A FEW IDEAS:

3 MOMENTS FROM TODAY THAT YOU'D LIKE TO REMEMBER	SOMETHING THAT YOU STRUGGLED WITH TODAY AND HOW YOU CAN GROW TOMORROW	YOUR THOUGHTS AND FEELINGS ABOUT YOUR MINDFULNESS ROUTINE

_____

_____

_____

_____

_____

_____

_____

_____

_____

HERE'S A TIP: THERE ARE ALSO A WHOLE BUNCH OF JOURNALING PROMPTS ON PAGES 40-41. CHECK THOSE OUT!

My daily Mindfulness JOURNAL

today i'm feeling:

draw your own

today I want to be more mindful by:

- ☐ having periods of silence
- ☐ appreciating the little but beautiful things in life
- ☐ taking deep breaths, especially when I feel stressed.
- ☐ listening to others well

❋ my daily mindfulness practice: ❋

Today I _____

for _____ [how long?]

before my mindfulness routine I...

felt these emotions:

was thinking about:

tried to concentrate on:

found this difficult:

really enjoyed:

afterward, I felt _____

and I learned _____

I CHOOSE TO FEEL: AND WILL FOCUS ON:

TODAY

TODAY I AM GRATEFUL FOR:

1.

2.

3.

My daily Mindfulness
JOURNAL

[date]

NOT SURE WHAT TO WRITE ABOUT? HERE'S A FEW IDEAS:

3 MOMENTS FROM TODAY THAT YOU'D LIKE TO REMEMBER

SOMETHING THAT YOU STRUGGLED WITH TODAY AND HOW YOU CAN GROW TOMORROW

YOUR THOUGHTS AND FEELINGS ABOUT YOUR MINDFULNESS ROUTINE

HERE'S A TIP: THERE ARE ALSO A WHOLE BUNCH OF JOURNALING PROMPTS ON PAGES 40-41. CHECK THOSE OUT!

My daily Mindfulness JOURNAL

today i'm feeling:

draw your own

today I want to be more mindful by:

- ☐ having periods of silence
- ☐ appreciating the little but beautiful things in life
- ☐ taking deep breaths, especially when I feel stressed.
- ☐ listening to others well

❋ my daily mindfulness practice: ❋

Today I _____

for _____ [how long?]

before my mindfulness routine I...

felt these emotions:

was thinking about:

tried to concentrate on:

found this difficult:

really enjoyed:

afterward, I felt _____

and I learned _____

I CHOOSE TO FEEL: AND WILL FOCUS ON:

TODAY

TODAY I AM GRATEFUL FOR:

1.

2.

3.

My daily Mindfulness
JOURNAL

NOT SURE WHAT TO WRITE ABOUT? HERE'S A FEW IDEAS:

3 MOMENTS FROM TODAY THAT YOU'D LIKE TO REMEMBER

SOMETHING THAT YOU STRUGGLED WITH TODAY AND HOW YOU CAN GROW TOMORROW

YOUR THOUGHTS AND FEELINGS ABOUT YOUR MINDFULNESS ROUTINE

HERE'S A TIP: THERE ARE ALSO A WHOLE BUNCH OF JOURNALING PROMPTS ON PAGES 40-41. CHECK THOSE OUT!

My daily Mindfulness JOURNAL

[daTe]

today i'm feeling:

draw your own

today I want to be more mindful by:

- ☐ having periods of silence
- ☐ appreciating the little but beautiful things in life
- ☐ taking deep breaths, especially when I feel stressed.
- ☐ listening to others well

❋ my daily mindfulness practice: ❋

Today I _____

for _____ [how long?]

before my mindfulness routine I...

felt these emotions:

was thinking about:

tried to concentrate on:

found this difficult:

really enjoyed:

afterward, I felt _____

and I learned _____

I CHOOSE TO FEEL: AND WILL FOCUS ON:

TODAY

TODAY I AM GRATEFUL FOR:

1.

2.

3.

My daily Mindfulness JOURNAL

[date]

NOT SURE WHAT TO WRITE ABOUT? HERE'S A FEW IDEAS:

| 3 MOMENTS FROM TODAY THAT YOU'D LIKE TO REMEMBER | SOMETHING THAT YOU STRUGGLED WITH TODAY AND HOW YOU CAN GROW TOMORROW | YOUR THOUGHTS AND FEELINGS ABOUT YOUR MINDFULNESS ROUTINE |

HERE'S A TIP: THERE ARE ALSO A WHOLE BUNCH OF JOURNALING PROMPTS ON PAGES 40-41. CHECK THOSE OUT!

My daily Mindfulness JOURNAL

today i'm feeling:

draw your own

today I want to be more mindful by:

- ☐ having periods of silence
- ☐ appreciating the little but beautiful things in life
- ☐ taking deep breaths, especially when I feel stressed.
- ☐ listening to others well

❋ my daily mindfulness practice: ❋

Today I _____

for _____ [how long?]

before my mindfulness routine I...

felt these emotions:

was thinking about:

tried to concentrate on:

found this difficult:

really enjoyed:

afterward, I felt _____

and I learned _____

I CHOOSE TO FEEL: AND WILL FOCUS ON:

TODAY

TODAY I AM
GRATEFUL
FOR:

1.
2.
3.

My daily Mindfulness JOURNAL

NOT SURE WHAT TO WRITE ABOUT? HERE'S A FEW IDEAS:

> **3 MOMENTS FROM TODAY THAT YOU'D LIKE TO REMEMBER**

> **SOMETHING THAT YOU STRUGGLED WITH TODAY AND HOW YOU CAN GROW TOMORROW**

> **YOUR THOUGHTS AND FEELINGS ABOUT YOUR MINDFULNESS ROUTINE**

HERE'S A TIP: THERE ARE ALSO A WHOLE BUNCH OF JOURNALING PROMPTS ON PAGES 40-41. CHECK THOSE OUT!

My daily Mindfulness JOURNAL

today i'm feeling:

draw your own

today I want to be more mindful by:

- ☐ having periods of silence
- ☐ appreciating the little but beautiful things in life
- ☐ taking deep breaths, especially when I feel stressed.
- ☐ listening to others well

❋ my daily mindfulness practice: ❋

Today I _____

for _____ [how long?]

before my mindfulness routine I...

felt these emotions:

was thinking about:

tried to concentrate on:

found this difficult:

really enjoyed:

afterward, I felt _____

and I learned _____

I CHOOSE TO FEEL: AND WILL FOCUS ON:

TODAY

TODAY I AM
GRATEFUL
FOR:
1.
2.
3.

My daily Mindfulness
JOURNAL

NOT SURE WHAT TO WRITE ABOUT? HERE'S A FEW IDEAS:

| 3 MOMENTS FROM TODAY THAT YOU'D LIKE TO REMEMBER | SOMETHING THAT YOU STRUGGLED WITH TODAY AND HOW YOU CAN GROW TOMORROW | YOUR THOUGHTS AND FEELINGS ABOUT YOUR MINDFULNESS ROUTINE |

_____

_____

_____

_____

_____

_____

_____

_____

HERE'S A TIP: THERE ARE ALSO A WHOLE BUNCH OF JOURNALING PROMPTS ON PAGES 40-41. CHECK THOSE OUT!

My daily Mindfulness JOURNAL

today i'm feeling:

draw your own

today I want to be more mindful by:

- ☐ having periods of silence
- ☐ appreciating the little but beautiful things in life
- ☐ taking deep breaths, especially when I feel stressed.
- ☐ listening to others well

❊ my daily mindfulness practice: ❊

Today I _____

for _____ [how long?]

before my mindfulness routine I...

felt these emotions:

was thinking about:

tried to concentrate on:

found this difficult:

really enjoyed:

afterward, I felt _____

and I learned _____

I CHOOSE TO FEEL: AND WILL FOCUS ON:

TODAY

TODAY I AM
GRATEFUL
FOR:

1.

2.

3.

My daily Mindfulness
JOURNAL

[date]

NOT SURE WHAT TO WRITE ABOUT? HERE'S A FEW IDEAS:

3 MOMENTS FROM TODAY THAT YOU'D LIKE TO REMEMBER

SOMETHING THAT YOU STRUGGLED WITH TODAY AND HOW YOU CAN GROW TOMORROW

YOUR THOUGHTS AND FEELINGS ABOUT YOUR MINDFULNESS ROUTINE

HERE'S A TIP: THERE ARE ALSO A WHOLE BUNCH OF JOURNALING PROMPTS ON PAGES 40-41. CHECK THOSE OUT!

My daily Mindfulness JOURNAL

[daTe]

today i'm feeling:

draw your own

today I want to be more mindful by:

- [ ] having periods of silence
- [ ] appreciating the little but beautiful things in life
- [ ] taking deep breaths, especially when I feel stressed.
- [ ] listening to others well

my daily mindfulness practice:

Today I ______________________

for ____________ [how long?]

before my mindfulness routine I...

felt these emotions:

was thinking about:

tried to concentrate on:

found this difficult:

really enjoyed:

afterward, I felt ______________

and I learned ______________

I CHOOSE TO FEEL: AND WILL FOCUS ON:

TODAY

TODAY I AM GRATEFUL FOR:

1.
2.
3.

My daily Mindfulness JOURNAL

[date]

NOT SURE WHAT TO WRITE ABOUT? HERE'S A FEW IDEAS:

3 MOMENTS FROM TODAY THAT YOU'D LIKE TO REMEMBER

SOMETHING THAT YOU STRUGGLED WITH TODAY AND HOW YOU CAN GROW TOMORROW

YOUR THOUGHTS AND FEELINGS ABOUT YOUR MINDFULNESS ROUTINE

HERE'S A TIP: THERE ARE ALSO A WHOLE BUNCH OF JOURNALING PROMPTS ON PAGES 40-41. CHECK THOSE OUT!

My daily Mindfulness JOURNAL

today i'm feeling:

draw your own

today I want to be more mindful by:

- ☐ having periods of silence
- ☐ appreciating the little but beautiful things in life
- ☐ taking deep breaths, especially when I feel stressed.
- ☐ listening to others well

❋ my daily mindfulness practice: ❋

Today I _____

for _____ [how long?]

before my mindfulness routine I...

felt these emotions:

was thinking about:

tried to concentrate on:

found this difficult:

really enjoyed:

afterward, I felt _____

and I learned _____

I CHOOSE TO FEEL: AND WILL FOCUS ON:

TODAY

TODAY I AM GRATEFUL FOR:
1.
2.
3.

My daily Mindfulness
JOURNAL

[date]

NOT SURE WHAT TO WRITE ABOUT? HERE'S A FEW IDEAS:

3 MOMENTS FROM TODAY THAT YOU'D LIKE TO REMEMBER

SOMETHING THAT YOU STRUGGLED WITH TODAY AND HOW YOU CAN GROW TOMORROW

YOUR THOUGHTS AND FEELINGS ABOUT YOUR MINDFULNESS ROUTINE

HERE'S A TIP: THERE ARE ALSO A WHOLE BUNCH OF JOURNALING PROMPTS ON PAGES 40-41. CHECK THOSE OUT!

My daily Mindfulness JOURNAL

today i'm feeling:

draw your own

today I want to be more mindful by:

- ☐ having periods of silence
- ☐ appreciating the little but beautiful things in life
- ☐ taking deep breaths, especially when I feel stressed.
- ☐ listening to others well

❋ my daily mindfulness practice: ❋

Today I _____

for _____ [how long?]

before my mindfulness routine I...

felt these emotions:

was thinking about:

tried to concentrate on:

found this difficult:

really enjoyed:

afterward, I felt _____

and I learned _____

I CHOOSE TO FEEL: AND WILL FOCUS ON:

TODAY

TODAY I AM
GRATEFUL
FOR:

1.
2.
3.

My daily Mindfulness JOURNAL

[daTe]

NOT SURE WHAT TO WRITE ABOUT? HERE'S A FEW IDEAS:

3 MOMENTS FROM TODAY THAT YOU'D LIKE TO REMEMBER

SOMETHING THAT YOU STRUGGLED WITH TODAY AND HOW YOU CAN GROW TOMORROW

YOUR THOUGHTS AND FEELINGS ABOUT YOUR MINDFULNESS ROUTINE

HERE'S A TIP: THERE ARE ALSO A WHOLE BUNCH OF JOURNALING PROMPTS ON PAGES 40-41. CHECK THOSE OUT!

My daily Mindfulness JOURNAL

[date]

today i'm feeling:

today I want to be more mindful by:

- [ ] having periods of silence
- [ ] appreciating the little but beautiful things in life
- [ ] taking deep breaths, especially when I feel stressed.
- [ ] listening to others well

my daily mindfulness practice:

Today I ____________________

for ____________ [how long?]

before my mindfulness routine I...

felt these emotions:

was thinking about:

tried to concentrate on:

found this difficult:

really enjoyed:

afterward, I felt ____________

and I learned ____________

TODAY

I CHOOSE TO FEEL:

AND WILL FOCUS ON:

TODAY I AM GRATEFUL FOR:

1.
2.
3.

My daily Mindfulness JOURNAL

_____ [date]

NOT SURE WHAT TO WRITE ABOUT? HERE'S A FEW IDEAS:

| 3 MOMENTS FROM TODAY THAT YOU'D LIKE TO REMEMBER | SOMETHING THAT YOU STRUGGLED WITH TODAY AND HOW YOU CAN GROW TOMORROW | YOUR THOUGHTS AND FEELINGS ABOUT YOUR MINDFULNESS ROUTINE |

_____

_____

_____

_____

_____

_____

_____

_____

_____

HERE'S A TIP: THERE ARE ALSO A WHOLE BUNCH OF JOURNALING PROMPTS ON PAGES 40-41. CHECK THOSE OUT!

My daily Mindfulness JOURNAL

today i'm feeling:

draw your own

today I want to be more mindful by:

- ☐ having periods of silence
- ☐ appreciating the little but beautiful things in life
- ☐ taking deep breaths, especially when I feel stressed.
- ☐ listening to others well

❋ my daily mindfulness practice: ❋

Today I _____

for _____ [how long?]

before my mindfulness routine I...

felt these emotions:

was thinking about:

tried to concentrate on:

found this difficult:

really enjoyed:

afterward, I felt _____

and I learned _____

I CHOOSE TO FEEL: AND WILL FOCUS ON:

TODAY

TODAY I AM GRATEFUL FOR:

1.
2.
3.

My daily Mindfulness
JOURNAL

[date]

NOT SURE WHAT TO WRITE ABOUT? HERE'S A FEW IDEAS:

3 MOMENTS FROM TODAY THAT YOU'D LIKE TO REMEMBER

SOMETHING THAT YOU STRUGGLED WITH TODAY AND HOW YOU CAN GROW TOMORROW

YOUR THOUGHTS AND FEELINGS ABOUT YOUR MINDFULNESS ROUTINE

HERE'S A TIP: THERE ARE ALSO A WHOLE BUNCH OF JOURNALING PROMPTS ON PAGES 40-41. CHECK THOSE OUT!

My daily Mindfulness JOURNAL

today i'm feeling:

draw your own

today I want to be more mindful by:

- ☐ having periods of silence
- ☐ appreciating the little but beautiful things in life
- ☐ taking deep breaths, especially when I feel stressed.
- ☐ listening to others well

✳ my daily mindfulness practice: ✳

Today I _____

for _____ [how long?]

before my mindfulness routine I...

felt these emotions:

was thinking about:

tried to concentrate on:

found this difficult:

really enjoyed:

afterward, I felt _____

and I learned _____

I CHOOSE TO FEEL: AND WILL FOCUS ON:

TODAY

TODAY I AM GRATEFUL FOR:

1.

2.

3.

My daily Mindfulness JOURNAL

[date]

NOT SURE WHAT TO WRITE ABOUT? HERE'S A FEW IDEAS:

3 MOMENTS FROM TODAY THAT YOU'D LIKE TO REMEMBER

SOMETHING THAT YOU STRUGGLED WITH TODAY AND HOW YOU CAN GROW TOMORROW

YOUR THOUGHTS AND FEELINGS ABOUT YOUR MINDFULNESS ROUTINE

HERE'S A TIP: THERE ARE ALSO A WHOLE BUNCH OF JOURNALING PROMPTS ON PAGES 40-41. CHECK THOSE OUT!

My daily Mindfulness JOURNAL

today i'm feeling:

draw your own

today I want to be more mindful by:

☐ having periods of silence

☐ appreciating the little but beautiful things in life

☐ taking deep breaths, especially when I feel stressed.

☐ listening to others well

❋ my daily mindfulness practice: ❋

Today I _____

for _____ [how long?]

before my mindfulness routine I...

felt these emotions:

was thinking about:

tried to concentrate on:

found this difficult:

really enjoyed:

afterward, I felt _____

and I learned _____

I CHOOSE TO FEEL: AND WILL FOCUS ON:

TODAY

TODAY I AM GRATEFUL FOR:

1.

2.

3.

My daily Mindfulness
JOURNAL

[daTe]

NOT SURE WHAT TO WRITE ABOUT? HERE'S A FEW IDEAS:

3 MOMENTS FROM TODAY THAT YOU'D LIKE TO REMEMBER

SOMETHING THAT YOU STRUGGLED WITH TODAY AND HOW YOU CAN GROW TOMORROW

YOUR THOUGHTS AND FEELINGS ABOUT YOUR MINDFULNESS ROUTINE

HERE'S A TIP: THERE ARE ALSO A WHOLE BUNCH OF JOURNALING PROMPTS ON PAGES 40-41. CHECK THOSE OUT!

My daily Mindfulness
JOURNAL

_____ [daTe]

today i'm feeling:

draw your own

today I want to be more mindful by:

- ☐ having periods of silence
- ☐ appreciating the little but beautiful things in life
- ☐ taking deep breaths, especially when I feel stressed.
- ☐ listening to others well

❋ my daily mindfulness practice: ❋

Today I _____

for _____ [how long?]

before my mindfulness routine I...

felt these emotions:

was thinking about:

tried to concentrate on:

found this difficult:

really enjoyed:

afterward, I felt _____

and I learned _____

I CHOOSE TO FEEL: AND WILL FOCUS ON:

TODAY

TODAY I AM GRATEFUL FOR:

1.

2.

3.

My daily Mindfulness
JOURNAL

[date]

NOT SURE WHAT TO WRITE ABOUT? HERE'S A FEW IDEAS:

| 3 MOMENTS FROM TODAY THAT YOU'D LIKE TO REMEMBER | SOMETHING THAT YOU STRUGGLED WITH TODAY AND HOW YOU CAN GROW TOMORROW | YOUR THOUGHTS AND FEELINGS ABOUT YOUR MINDFULNESS ROUTINE |

_____

_____

_____

_____

_____

_____

_____

_____

_____

HERE'S A TIP: THERE ARE ALSO A WHOLE BUNCH OF JOURNALING PROMPTS ON PAGES 40-41. CHECK THOSE OUT!

My daily Mindfulness
JOURNAL

today i'm feeling:

draw your own

today I want to be more mindful by:

- ☐ having periods of silence
- ☐ appreciating the little but beautiful things in life
- ☐ taking deep breaths, especially when I feel stressed.
- ☐ listening to others well

❋ my daily mindfulness practice: ❋

Today I _____

for _____ [how long?]

before my mindfulness routine I...

felt these emotions:

was thinking about:

tried to concentrate on:

found this difficult:

really enjoyed:

afterward, I felt _____

and I learned _____

I CHOOSE TO FEEL: AND WILL FOCUS ON:

TODAY

TODAY I AM GRATEFUL FOR:	
	1.
	2.
	3.

My daily Mindfulness
JOURNAL

NOT SURE WHAT TO WRITE ABOUT? HERE'S A FEW IDEAS:

3 MOMENTS FROM TODAY THAT YOU'D LIKE TO REMEMBER

SOMETHING THAT YOU STRUGGLED WITH TODAY AND HOW YOU CAN GROW TOMORROW

YOUR THOUGHTS AND FEELINGS ABOUT YOUR MINDFULNESS ROUTINE

_____

_____

_____

_____

_____

_____

_____

_____

HERE'S A TIP: THERE ARE ALSO A WHOLE BUNCH OF JOURNALING PROMPTS ON PAGES 40-41. CHECK THOSE OUT!

My daily Mindfulness JOURNAL

today i'm feeling:

draw your own

today I want to be more mindful by:

- ☐ having periods of silence
- ☐ appreciating the little but beautiful things in life
- ☐ taking deep breaths, especially when I feel stressed.
- ☐ listening to others well

✳ my daily mindfulness practice: ✳

Today I _____

for _____ [how long?]

before my mindfulness routine I...

felt these emotions:

was thinking about:

tried to concentrate on:

found this difficult:

really enjoyed:

afterward, I felt _____

and I learned _____

I CHOOSE TO FEEL: AND WILL FOCUS ON:

TODAY

TODAY I AM
GRATEFUL
FOR:

1.

2.

3.

My daily Mindfulness
JOURNAL

[date]

NOT SURE WHAT TO WRITE ABOUT? HERE'S A FEW IDEAS:

3 MOMENTS FROM TODAY THAT YOU'D LIKE TO REMEMBER

SOMETHING THAT YOU STRUGGLED WITH TODAY AND HOW YOU CAN GROW TOMORROW

YOUR THOUGHTS AND FEELINGS ABOUT YOUR MINDFULNESS ROUTINE

_____

_____

_____

_____

_____

_____

_____

_____

_____

HERE'S A TIP: THERE ARE ALSO A WHOLE BUNCH OF JOURNALING PROMPTS ON PAGES 40-41. CHECK THOSE OUT!

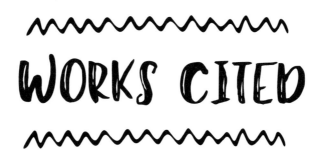

WORKS CITED

[2021] "How can Nature Benefit my Mental Health?" Published November 20201 on Mind.Org. Retrieved June 2023. Link: https://www.mind.org.uk/information-support/tips-for-everyday-living/nature-and-mental-health/how-nature-benefits-mental-health/#:~:text=Nature%20and%20mental%20health%20problems,with%20mild%20to%20moderate%20depression.- © Mind. This information is published in full at www.mind.org.uk

8 Wellbeing Benefits of Practicing Gratitude / The Mindfulness Project Blog. (n.d.). 8 Wellbeing Benefits of Practicing Gratitude / the Mindfulness Project Blog. https://www.londonmindful.com/blog/8-wellbeing-benefits-of-practicing-gratitude/

Gratitude [noun] - Definition, pictures, pronunciation and usage notes | Oxford Advanced Learner's Dictionary at OxfordLearnersDictionaries.com. (n.d.). Information retrieved June 2023, from https://www.oxfordlearnersdictionaries.com/definition/english/gratitude

How Mindfulness and Gratitude Can Improve Your Well-Being | Ochsner Health. (n.d.). Ochsner Health System. https://blog.ochsner.org/articles/giving-thanks-how-mindfulness-and-gratitude-can-improve-your-well-being

Staff, M. (2020, July 8). What is Mindfulness? - Mindful. Mindful. https://www.mindful.org/what-is-mindfulness/

(2019) "Mindfulness Meditation: A Research Proven way to reduce stress" American Psychological Association. Published digitally on October 30 2019. Written in collaboration with J. David Creswell, PhD, and Bassam Khoury, PhD,. Retrieved June 2023 from: https://www.apa.org/topics/mindfulness/meditation Mindfulness: 5 Powerful Exercises for Peace and Happiness. https://www.consciouslifestylemag.com/mindfulness-powerful-exercises-peace-of-mind/

Natha, D. (2022, December 30). Navigating Panic Attacks | Oceanside Psychology Clinic. Oceanside Psychology Clinic |. https://oceansideclinic.com/navigating-panic-attacks/ Embrace the Stillness. (2019, November 25). Alisasroom - Insight and Sharing. https://alisasroom.com/2019/11/25/embrace-the-stillness/

How Does Nature Impact Our Wellbeing? | Taking Charge of Your Health & Wellbeing. (2023, January 1). Taking Charge of Your Health & Wellbeing. https://www.takingcharge.csh.umn.edu/how-does-nature-impact-our-wellbeing

NEED SOME MORE

daily Mindfulness
JOURNALING
PAGES?

 SCAN ME

SCAN THE QR CODE OR VISIT:

https://bonus.teen-thrive.com/mindfulnessjournalingpages

a brief message from

TEEN THRIVE

Hi there!

We hope you enjoyed the book. We would love to hear your thoughts on the book. Many readers don't know how hard reviews are to come by, and how much they help authors and publishers.

We would be incredibly grateful if you could take just 60 seconds to write a short review on Amazon, even if it's just a sentence or two!

Visit www.teen-thrive.com/review for instructions on how to leave a review. Thank you for taking the time to share your thoughts. Every single review makes a difference to us!

Signing off,
Teen Thrive

Made in the USA
Thornton, CO
03/11/24 18:55:15